Journeys

Direct Instruction Reading

Level 1
Answer Key

Siegfried Engelmann
Owen Engelmann
Karen Lou Seitz Davis

SRA

A Division of The McGraw-Hill Companies

Columbus, Ohio

SRA/McGraw-Hill

A Division of The **McGraw·Hill** *Companies*

Send all inquiries to:
SRA/McGraw-Hill
8787 Orion Place
Columbus, OH 43240-4027

ISBN 0-02-683523-1

2 3 4 5 6 7 8 9 MAZ 03 02 01 00

Worksheet 1 — Side 1

1. s a t
2. f a t

Colored.

Colored.

Colored.

o a

Side 1

Worksheet

Worksheet 1 — Side 2

a — y
k — n
y — e
n — a
e — k

mean	seem	me
~~me~~	meal	3
meet	~~me~~	
meal	see	~~me~~
meet	seen	
mean	feel	

ll = blue
ee = brown
y = green

ll ee y

S S S S S S S S S S S S

r r r r r r | t t t t t t t

Side 2

Worksheet

Worksheet 2 — Side 1

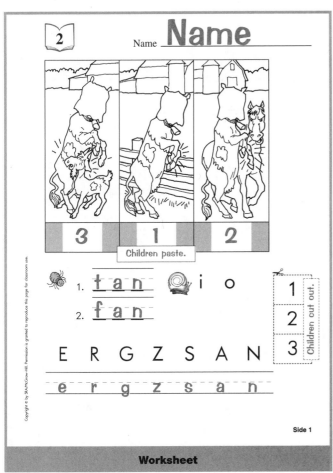

3   1   2

Children paste.

1. t a n   i o
2. f a n

| 1 |
| 2 |
| 3 |

Children cut out.

E R G Z S A N

e r g z s a n

Side 1

Worksheet

Worksheet 2 — Side 2

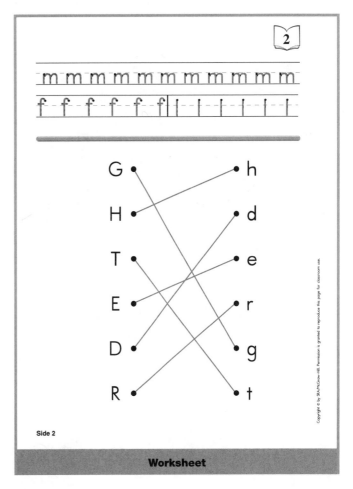

m m m m m m m m m m m

f f f f f f | t t t t t t

G •   • h
H •   • d
T •   • e
E •   • r
D •   • g
R •   • t

Side 2

Worksheet

3

Name _____

1. <u>ram</u>   2. <u>me</u>

3

ram •

seal •
Blue

man •

Side 1

Worksheet

Side 2

Worksheet

4

Name _____

Side 1

Worksheet

4

Side 2

Worksheet

4

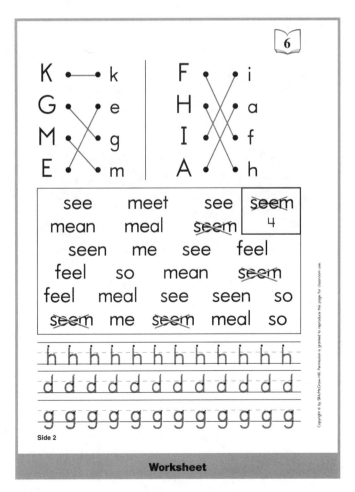

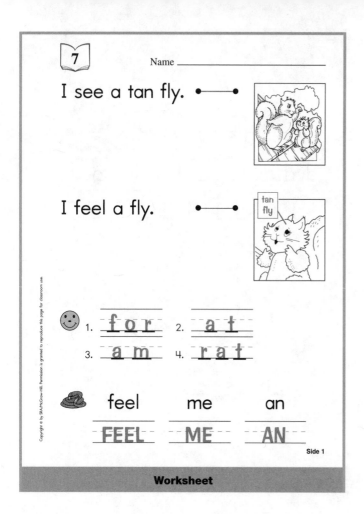

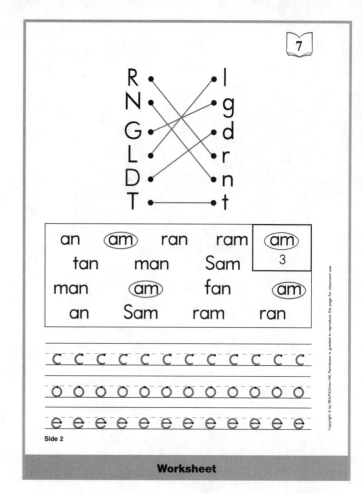

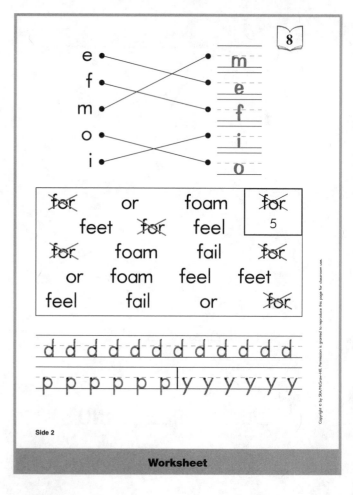

6

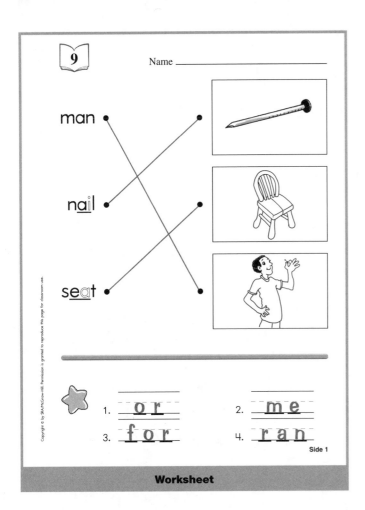

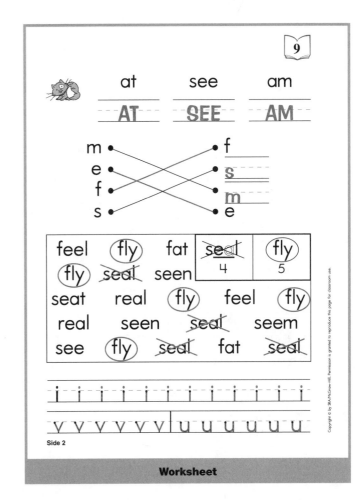

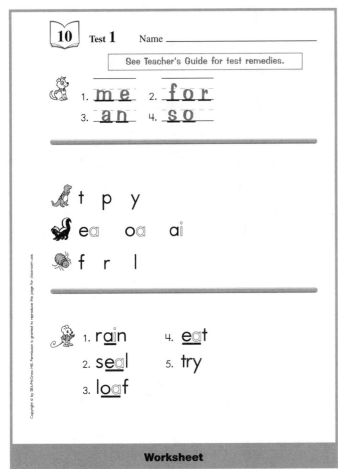

9

man

n**ai**l

s**ea**t

Side 1

1. __o r__   2. __m e__
3. __f o r__   4. __r a n__

Worksheet

9

at   see   am
AT   SEE   AM

m   f
e   s
f   m
s   e

feel	fly	fat	s̶e̶a̶l̶ 4	fly 5
fly	s̶e̶a̶l̶	seen		
seat	real	fly	feel	fly
real	seen	s̶e̶a̶l̶	seem	
see	fly	s̶e̶a̶l̶	fat	s̶e̶a̶l̶

i i i i i i i i i i i

v v v v v v v | u u u u u u

Side 2

Worksheet

10   Test **1**   Name _____

See Teacher's Guide for test remedies.

1. __m e__   2. __f o r__
3. __a n__   4. __s o__

t   p   y

e**a**   o**a**   **ai**

f   r   l

1. r**ai**n   4. **ea**t
2. s**ea**l   5. try
3. l**oa**f

Worksheet

Cutout, pasted and colored.

Child takes home.   **10**

ram   s**ea**l

fan   l**oa**f

r**ai**n   **ea**r

Take Home

Name _____

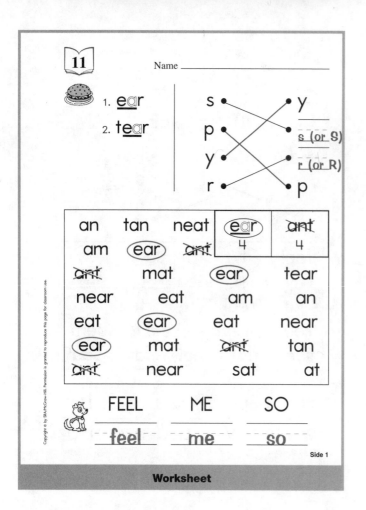

1. <u>ear</u>

2. t<u>ear</u>

s • ——— • y
p • ——— • ___
y • ——— • s (or S)
r • ——— • r (or R)
         • p

an	tan	neat	(ear)	~~ant~~
am	(ear)	~~ant~~	4	4
~~ant~~	mat	(ear)	tear	
near	eat	am	an	
eat	(ear)	eat	near	
(ear)	mat	~~ant~~	tan	
~~ant~~	near	sat	at	

FEEL	ME	SO
<u>feel</u>	<u>me</u>	<u>so</u>

Side 1

Worksheet

<u>My fan ran</u>.

My fan ran.

1. <u>no</u> 2. <u>am</u> 3. <u>me</u>

p p p p p p p p p p p p
h h h h h h h h h h h h
e e e e e e e e e e e e

Side 2

Worksheet

Name _____

d d d d d d d d d d d d
p p p p p p p p p p p p
r r r r r r r r r r r r

Cut out and pasted above.

Side 1

Worksheet

RAM	SEEN	NO
<u>ram</u>	<u>seen</u>	<u>no</u>

a • ⨯ • l   f • ⨯ • e
m • ⨯ • m   e • ⨯ • f
l • • a   r • • r

are	~~ant~~	(eat)	(eat)	~~ant~~
ear	near	ear	4	3
an	(eat)	tan	ear	am
fat	am	~~ant~~	neat	(eat)
am	tan	(eat)	fear	
near	an	~~ant~~	ear	at

1. <u>or</u> 2. <u>for</u> 3. <u>am</u>

Side 2

Worksheet

Name _____

I feel rain.

See me sail.

Cut out and pasted above.

Side 1

Worksheet

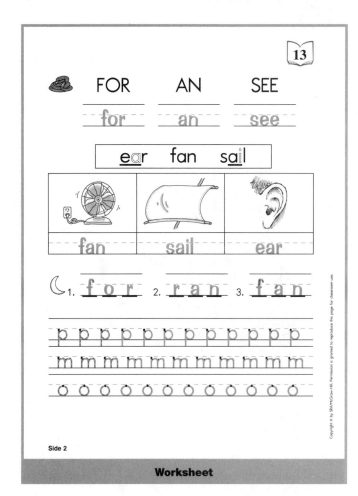

FOR   AN   SEE

for   an   see

ear   fan   sail

fan   sail   ear

1. for   2. ran   3. fan

p p p p p p p p p p p

m m m m m m m m m m m

o o o o o o o o o o o

Side 2

Worksheet

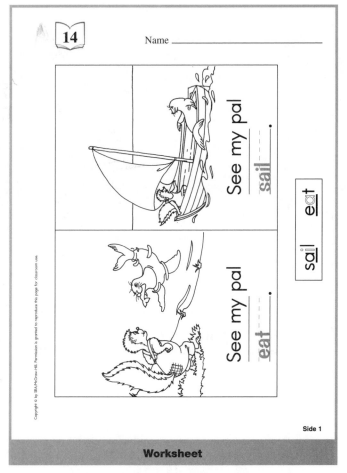

Name _____

See my pal
sail ___.

See my pal
eat ___.

sail   eat

Side 1

Worksheet

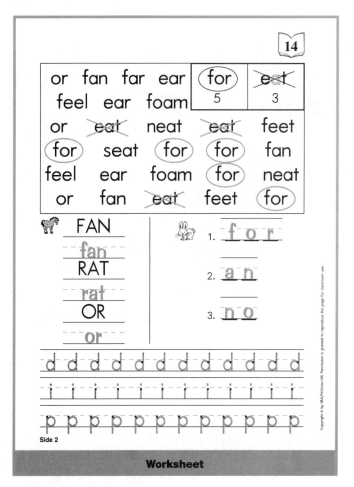

or fan far ear   for   eat
feel ear foam   5   3
or   eat neat   eat   feet
for   seat   for   for   fan
feel   ear   foam   for   neat
or   fan   eat   feet   for

FAN   1. for
fan
RAT   2. an
rat
OR   3. no
or

d d d d d d d d d d d

i i i i i i i i i i i

p p p p p p p p p p p

Side 2

Worksheet

9

Name _____

my pal

I am near my pal .

Side 1

Worksheet

---

mole fan so_a_p sa_i_l

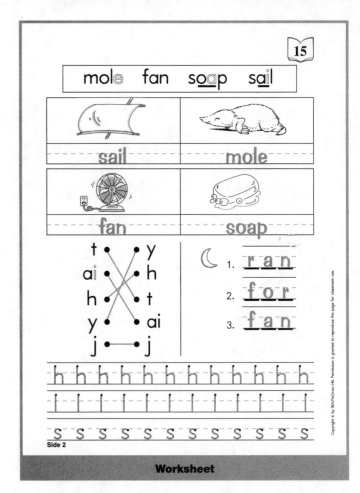

sail | mole
fan | soap

t • • y
ai • • h
h • • t
y • • ai
j • • j

1. r a n
2. f o r
3. f a n

h h h h h h h h h h h h h

l l l l l l l l l l l l

S S S S S S S S S S S S

Side 2

Worksheet

15

Child folds into a booklet and takes home.

A Fan

Page 1

**Lesson 15
Take Home
A Fan**

Name _____

I ran at a ram.

A ram ran at me.

1. A ram ran .
2. A ram ran .

Side 1

Worksheet

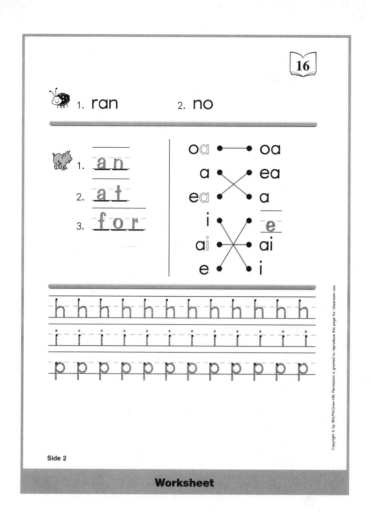

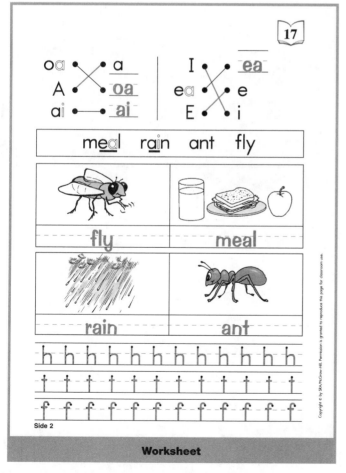

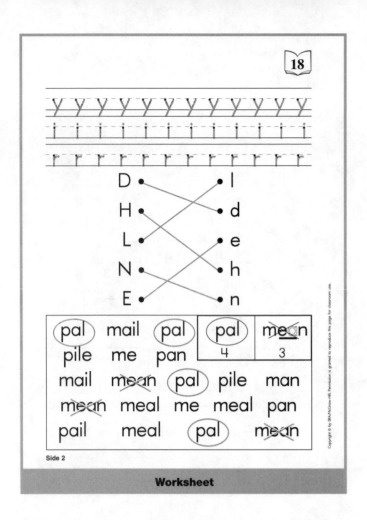

y y y y y y y y y y y

i i i i i i i i i i i

r r r r r r r r r r r

D •   • l
H •   • d
L •   • e
N •   • h
E •   • n

pal	mail	pal	pal	mean
pile	me	pan	4	3
mail	mean	pal	pile	man
mean	meal	me	meal	pan
pail	meal	pal	mean	

Side 2

Worksheet

Name _____

A fly sat.
A fly sat.
A fly sat.

1. s a t   2. m a t
3. m a n   4. o r

Side 1

Worksheet

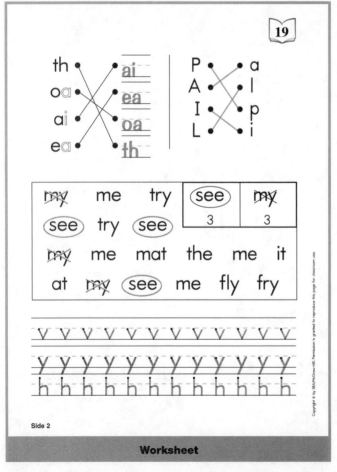

th •   • ai   P •   • a
oa •   • ea   A •   • l
ai •   • oa   I •   • p
ea •   • th   L •   • i

my	me	try	see	my
see	try	see	3	3
my	me	mat	the	me	it
at	my	see	me	fly	fry

v v v v v v v v v v v v

y y y y y y y y y y y y

h h h h h h h h h h h h

Side 2

Worksheet

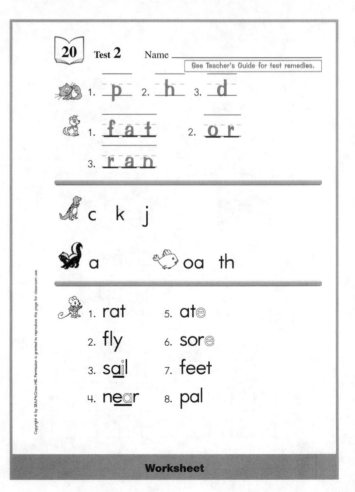

Test **2**   Name _____

See Teacher's Guide for test remedies.

1. p   2. h   3. d

1. f a t   2. o r

3. r a n

c   k   j

a   oa   th

1. rat   5. ate
2. fly   6. sore
3. sail   7. feet
4. near   8. pal

Worksheet

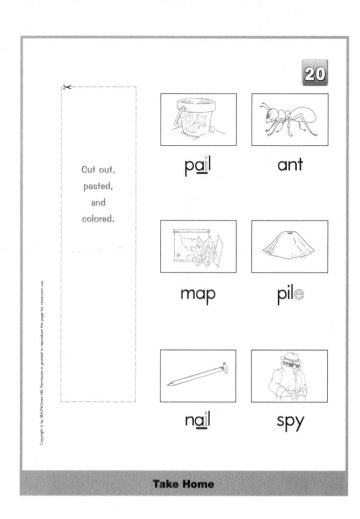

20

Cut out,
pasted,
and
colored.

pa<u>i</u>l   ant

map   pil<u>e</u>

n<u>ai</u>l   spy

21

Name _____

Colored.

I am a fly.
I fly n<u>ea</u>r an <u>ea</u>r.

Side 1

21

mat
rat
fat
Sam
at
fan

Sam

fan

e e e e e e e e e e e e e

p p p p p p p p p p p p p

y y y y y y y y y y y y y

Fly near me.
Fly near me.
Fly near me.

Side 2

22

Name _____

I rop<u>e</u> a ram.
See my pal fly.

See my pal fly.

t<u>ai</u>l •   • meal
m<u>ea</u>l •   • feel
fat •   • tail
feel •   • fat

Side 1

13

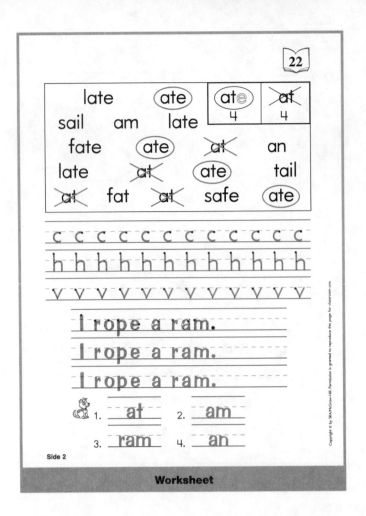

late   ate | ate | at |
sail   am   late | 4 | 4 |
fate   ate   at   an
late   at   ate   tail
at   fat   at   safe   ate

c c c c c c c c c c c

h h h h h h h h h h h

v v v v v v v v v v v

I rope a ram.
I rope a ram.
I rope a ram.

1. at   2. am
3. ram   4. an

Side 2

Worksheet

Name _____

I see a man fly.
I eat a meal.

I eat a meal.

rope •   • feet
pile •   • feel
feet •   • pile
feel •   • rope

Side 1

Worksheet

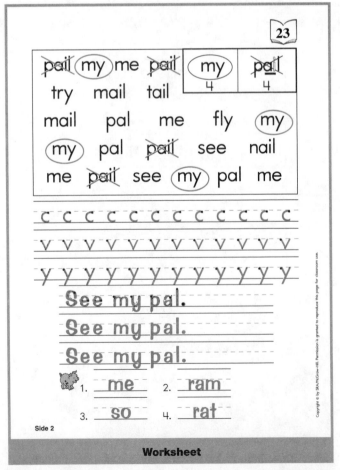

pail   my   me   pail | my | pal |
try   mail   tail | 4 | 4 |
mail   pal   me   fly   my
my   pal   pail   see   nail
me   pail   see   my   pal   me

c c c c c c c c c c c c

v v v v v v v v v v v v

y y y y y y y y y y y y

See my pal.
See my pal.
See my pal.

1. me   2. ram
3. so   4. rat

Side 2

Worksheet

Name _____

man   ran   mile   ram

The ram ran at the man.
So that man ran for
a mile.

me   my   meet | me | my |
my   me   meal | 4 | 4 |
me   mail   meet   mean   may
my   may   my   me   mean

Side 1

Worksheet

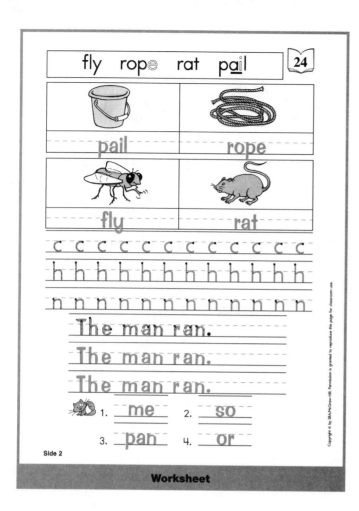

fly rope rat pail [24]

pail	rope
fly	rat

c c c c c c c c c c c c c

h h h h h h h h h h h h h

n n n n n n n n n n n n n

The man ran.

The man ran.

The man ran.

1. me   2. so

3. pan   4. or

Side 2

Worksheet

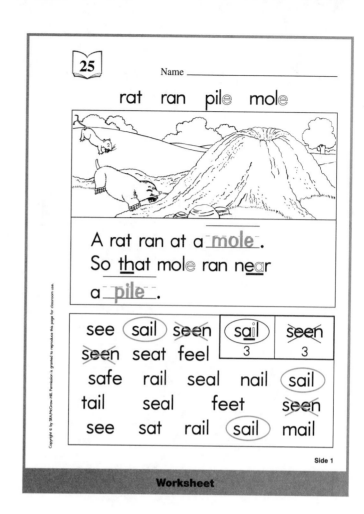

Name _____

rat ran pile mole

A rat ran at a _mole_.
So _that_ mole ran ne_a_r
a _pile_.

see ⬭sail⬭ seen	⬭sail⬭	~~seen~~
~~seen~~ seat feel	3	3

safe rail seal nail ⬭sail⬭

tail seal feet ~~seen~~

see sat rail ⬭sail⬭ mail

Side 1

Worksheet

n_ai_l l_oa_f _ea_r fan [25]

loaf	fan
ear	nail

d d d d d d d d d d d d

v v v v v v v v v v v v v

h h h h h h h h h h h h h

So the mole ran.

So the mole ran.

So the mole ran.

1. sat   2. for

3. pat   4. mat

Side 2

Worksheet

[25]

The Fly

Child folds
into a
booklet
and takes
home.

Page 1

Lesson 25
Take Home
The Fly

15

Name _____

soap tail rope

I made a ___rope___ .

pal •   • pan
pan •   • an
an   •   • man
man •   • pal

mole	rain	mad

mole	mad	rain

Side 1

Worksheet

---

ea = green
ai = brown
th = orange

ea ai th

d d d d d d d d d d d d d

y y y y y y y y y y y y y

p p p p p p p p p p p p p

I made a rope.

I made a rope.

I made a rope.

1. tap   2. ran

3. sat   4. an

Side 2

Worksheet

Name _____

tail soap me

I see foam and a ___tail___ .

I see no ___soap___ near me.

feet	sit	pail

pail	sit	feet

Side 1

Worksheet

~~fine~~ day (did) dad	(did)	~~fine~~
fly foam fat	3	3

fin and day (did) for
dad try pine fin ~~fine~~
fan (did) ~~fine~~ pine dad

d d d d d d d d d d d d d

t t t t t t t t t t t t t

p p p p p p p p p p p p p

I see no soap.

I see no soap.

I see no soap.

1. an   2. and

3. mad   4. pan

Side 2

Worksheet

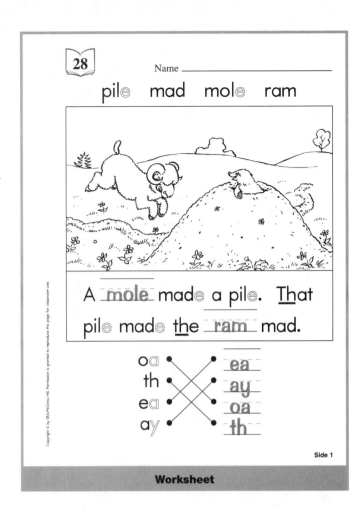

Name _____

pile mad mole ram

A _mole_ made a pile. That pile made the _ram_ mad.

oa
th
ea
ay

ea
ay
oa
th

Side 1

Worksheet

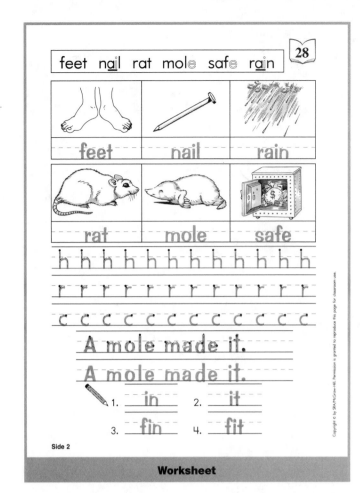

feet nail rat mole safe rain

feet   nail   rain

rat   mole   safe

h h h h h h h h h h h h

r r r r r r r r r r r r

c c c c c c c c c c c c

A mole made it.

A mole made it.

1. in   2. it

3. fin   4. fit

Side 2

Worksheet

Name _____

math   rain

It is time for _math_.

rat
seal
soap
mat

Side 1

Worksheet

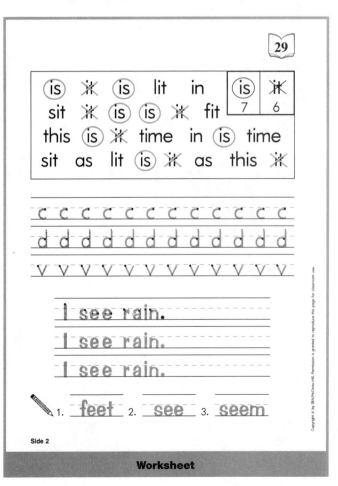

is ✳ is lit in | is | ✳ |
sit ✳ is is ✳ fit | 7 | 6 |
this is ✳ time in is time
sit as lit is ✳ as this ✳

c c c c c c c c c c c c

d d d d d d d d d d d d

v v v v v v v v v v v v

I see rain.

I see rain.

I see rain.

1. feet   2. see   3. seem

Side 2

Worksheet

17

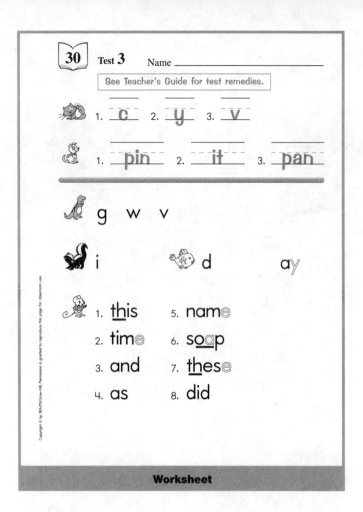

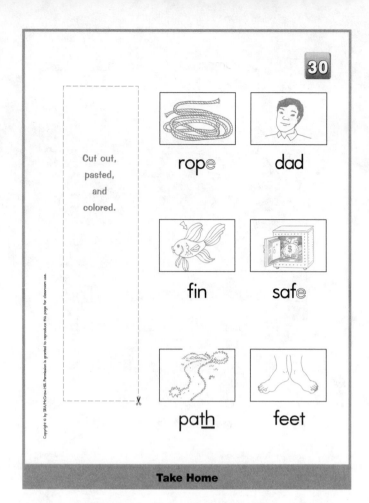

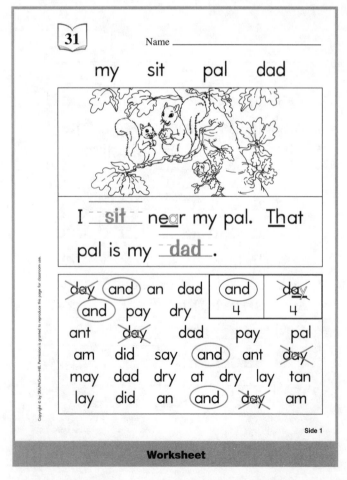

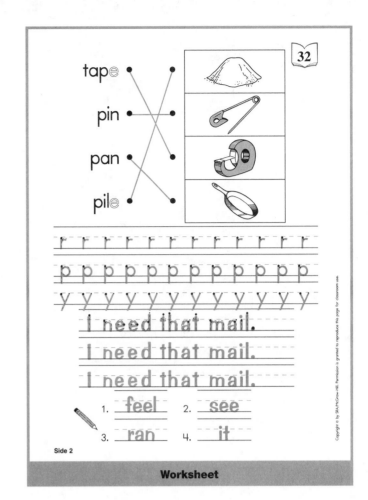

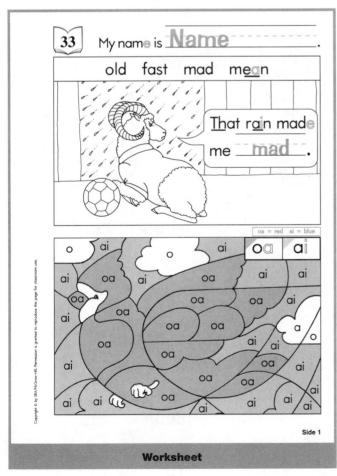

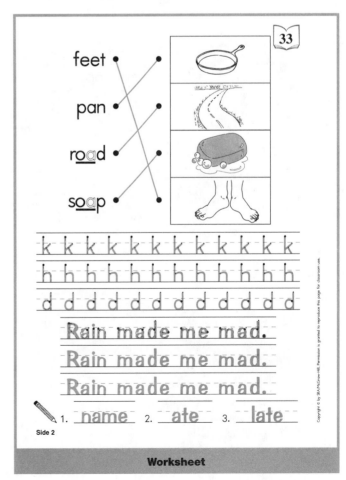

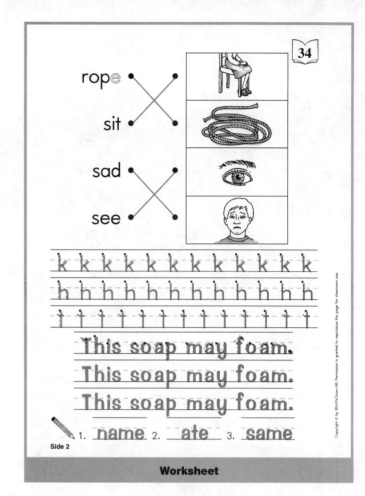

Rain

35

I see rain.

Page 1

Child folds into a booklet and takes home.

Lesson 35
Take Home
Rain

36 My name is _____.

A seal and a ram may play.

A seal may sleep.

Cut out and pasted above.

Side 1

Worksheet

tape   sit   leap

36

leap   tape   sit

j j j j j j j j j j j j

v v v v v v v v v v v v

p p p p p p p p p p p p

A ram may play.

A ram may play.

1. time   2. safe   3. late

Side 2

Worksheet

37 My name is _____.

see   rain   play   eat

My pal may ___play___
in the ___rain___ .

the	these	that	than	the
as	this	than	4	3
the		that	than	is
this	than		these	the
than		that		those

Side 1

Worksheet

j**ai**l   tree   sleep   p**a**t**h**

jail   path   sleep   tree

T • • c
C • • g
G • • t

M • • h
H • • m
R • • r

k k k k k k k k k k k k

j j j j j j j j j j j j

y y y y y y y y y y y y

I play in rain.

I play in rain.

I play in rain.

1. ant   2. pat   3. sat

Side 2

Worksheet

My nam**e** is _____ .

sor**e**   t**ai**l   pal   rid**e**

I lik**e** my
_____ pal .

My pal m**ay** tak**e** me
for a ___ride___ .

M • • h
H • • c
T • • m
G • • g
C • • t

Side 1

Worksheet

---

tree   div**e**   van   p**ai**l

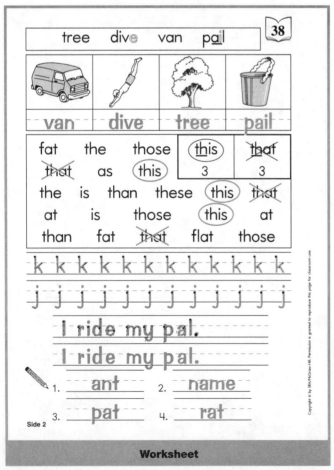

van   dive   tree   pail

fat	the	those	(this)	t̶h̶a̶t̶
t̶h̶a̶t̶	as	(this)	3	3
the	is	than	these	(this)	t̶h̶a̶t̶
at	is	those	(this)	at
than	fat	t̶h̶a̶t̶	flat	those

k k k k k k k k k k k k

j j j j j j j j j j j j

I ride my pal.

I ride my pal.

1. ant   2. name

3. pat   4. rat

Side 2

Worksheet

My nam**e** is _____ .

Pasted
below.

An ant is in a pin**e** tree.
__Th__at ant is saf**e**.

seal = brown   fine = blue

| s**ea**l | fin**e** |

Side 1

Worksheet

22

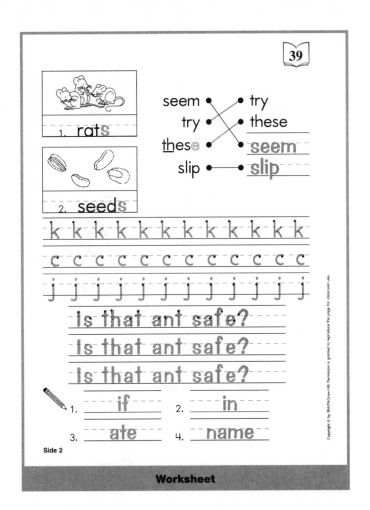

1. rat**s**

2. seed**s**

seem • — • try
try • ╳ • these
_the_e • ╳ • **seem**
slip • — • **slip**

k k k k k k k k k k k

c c c c c c c c c c c

j j j j j j j j j j j j

Is that ant safe?
Is that ant safe?
Is that ant safe?

1. ___ if ___ 2. ___ in ___
3. ___ ate ___ 4. ___ name ___

Side 2

Worksheet

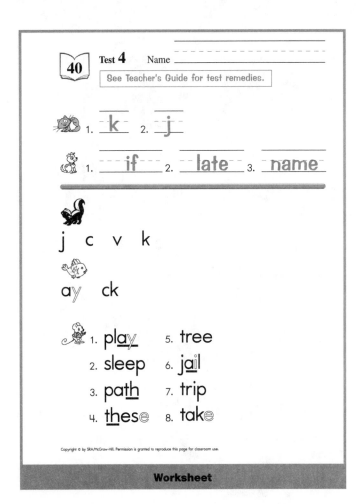

See Teacher's Guide for test remedies.

1. k   2. j

1. if   2. late   3. name

j c v k

a_y_   ck

1. pla_y_   5. tree
2. sleep   6. j_ai_l
3. pa_th_   7. trip
4. _the_e   8. tak_e_

Copyright © by SRA/McGraw-Hill. Permission is granted to reproduce this page for classroom use.

Worksheet

An ant is in a
pine tree.

It is a tail.

It is time for
the mail.

I see _the_ se_a_l
sleep.
40

Cut out, pasted, and folded into booklet.

fold first

fold

Copyright © by SRA/McGraw-Hill. Permission is granted to reproduce this page for classroom use.

Take Home

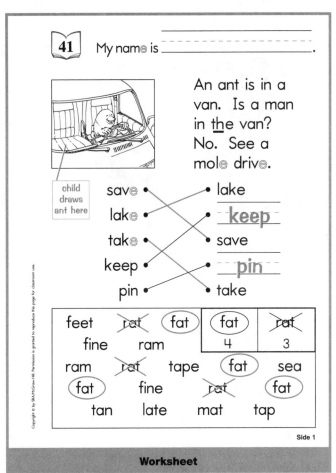

An ant is in a
van. Is a man
in _the_ van?
No. See a
mol_e_ drive.

child
draws
ant here

sav_e_ • — • lake
lak_e_ • ╳ • **keep**
tak_e_ • ╳ • save
keep • — • **pin**
pin • — • take

feet ~~rat~~ (fat)   (fat) | ~~rat~~
fine ram   4 | 3
ram ~~rat~~ tape (fat)   sea
(fat) fine ~~rat~~ (fat)
tan late mat tap

Copyright © by SRA/McGraw-Hill. Permission is granted to reproduce this page for classroom use.

Side 1

Worksheet

23

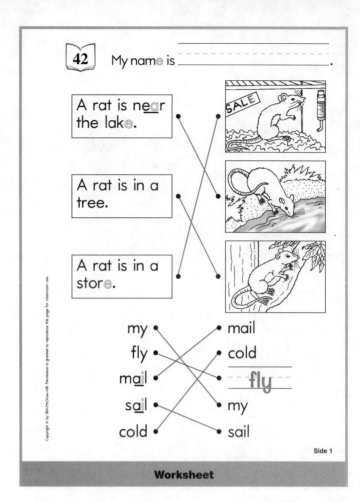

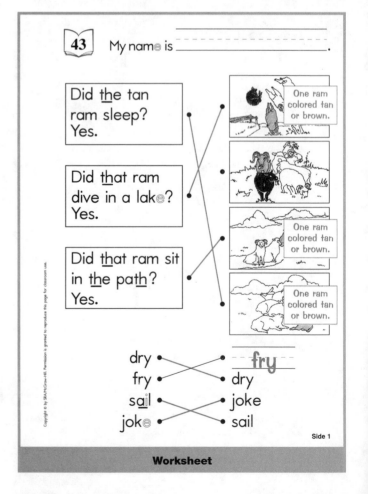

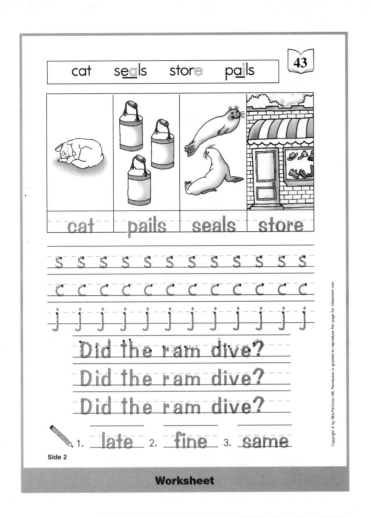

43

cat   se_a_ls   store   pa_i_ls

cat | pails | seals | store

s s s s s s s s s s s s

c c c c c c c c c c c c

j j j j j j j j j j j j

Did the ram dive?
Did the ram dive?
Did the ram dive?

1. late   2. fine   3. same

Side 2

Worksheet

44   My name is _____.

A se_a_l and 3 pals sat ne_a_r a lake.

Those pals ma_y_ pla_y_ in the lake.

Or those pals ma_y_ take a nap.

Side 1

Worksheet

44

cat   stove   tape   ta_i_l   kite   ram

kites | ram | tails

tape | cats | stove

c c c c c c c c c c c

d d d d d d d d d d d

p p p p p p p p p p p

Those pals may play.
Those pals may play.
Those pals may play.

1. fan   2. same
3. pine   4. tame

Side 2

Worksheet

---

45   My name is _____.

cats   trip   path   rakes

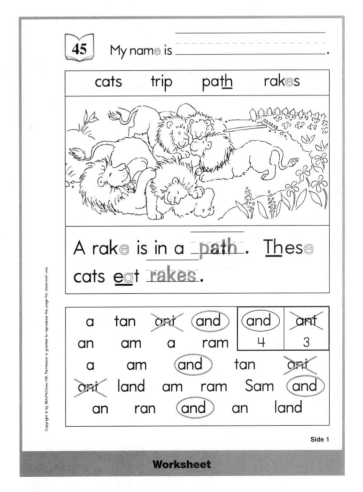

A rake is in a __path__. These cats e_a_t __rakes__.

a	tan	~~ant~~	(and)	(and)	~~ant~~
an	am	a	ram	4	3
a	am	(and)	tan	~~ant~~	
~~ant~~	land	am	ram	Sam	(and)
an	ran	(and)	an	land	

Side 1

Worksheet

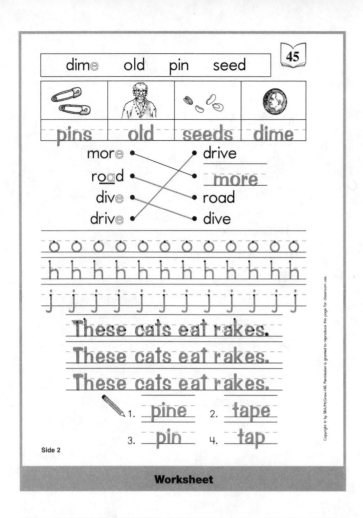

Side 2

Worksheet

Me and My Pal

Child folds into a booklet and takes home.

Page 1

**Lesson 45
Take Home
Me and My Pal**

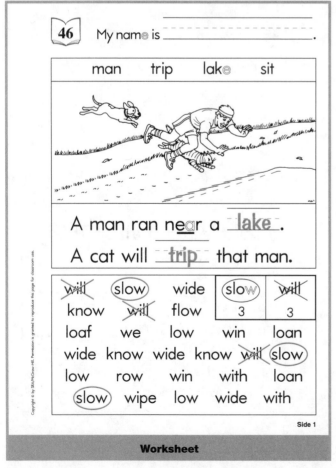

Side 1

Worksheet

Side 2

Worksheet

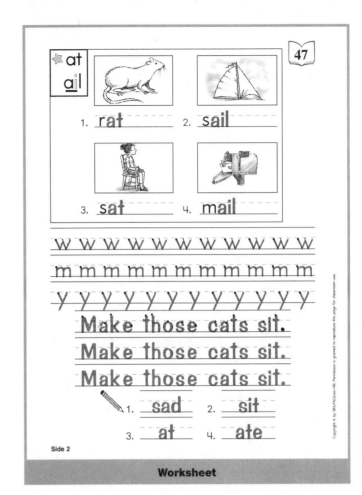

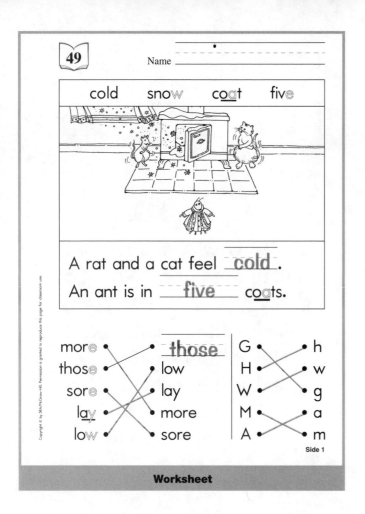

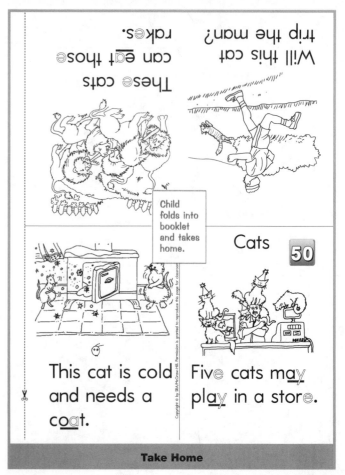

49 Name _____

cold   snow   c__oa__t   fiv__e__

A rat and a cat feel __cold__.
An ant is in __five__ co__a__ts.

mor__e__	those
thos__e__	low
sor__e__	lay
la__y__	more
low	sore

G	h
H	w
W	g
M	a
A	m

Side 1

Worksheet

49

r__ea__d mad __ea__t rake sleep driv__e__

eat   rake   drive

read   sleep   mad

s s s s s s s s s s s
w w w w w w w w w w w
c c c c c c c c c c c

The rat feels cold.
The rat feels cold.
The rat feels cold.

1. __rain__ 2. __aim__ 3. __sail__

Side 2

Worksheet

---

50 Test **5** Name _____

See Teacher's Guide for test remedies.

__w__   g w

1. __mail__ 2. __rain__ 3. __aim__

A man and a cat ran n__ea__r a lak__e__.

1. driv__e__	1. snow	1. you
2. will	2. tr__ai__ns	2. s__ai__d
3. jok__e__	3. stor__e__s	3. if

Worksheet

These cats
can e__a__t thos__e__
rak__e__s.

Will this cat
trip the man?

Child folds into booklet and takes home.

Cats **50**

This cat is cold and needs a c__oa__t.

Fiv__e__ cats m__ay__ pl__ay__ in a stor__e__.

Take Home

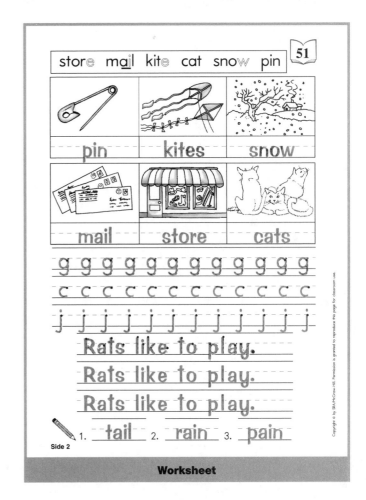

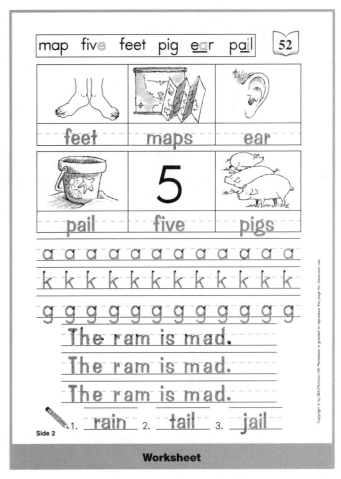

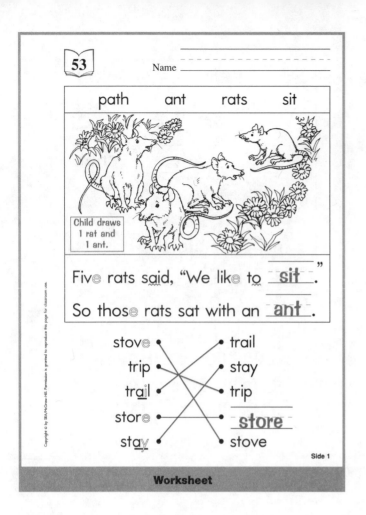

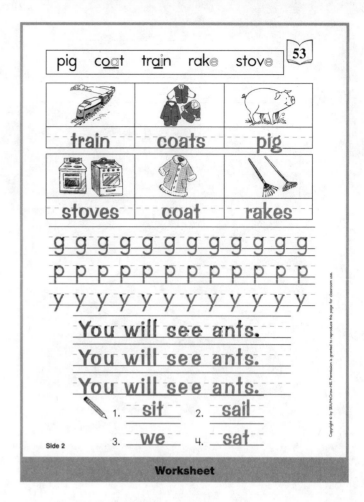

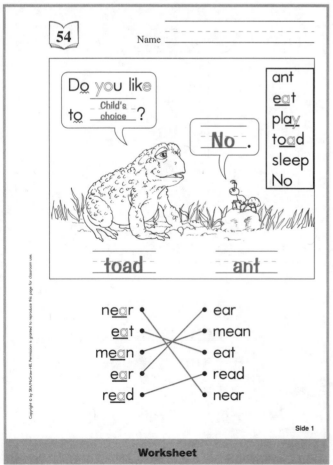

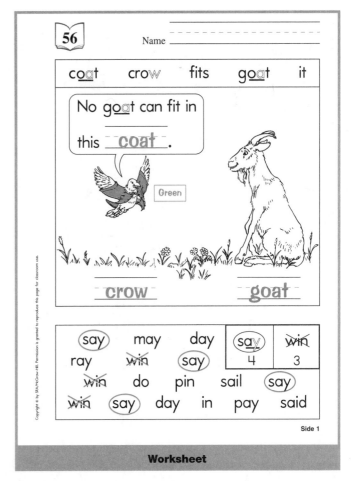

mad rain mail seeds toad cave

seeds	rain	cave
toad	mail	mad

w w w w w w w w w w w

d d d d d d d d d d d d

g g g g g g g g g g g g

The coat will fit.
The coat will fit.
The coat will fit.

1. rain   2. meal
3. mail   4. mean

Side 2

Worksheet

Name

coat   ate   crow   goat   it

You _ate_ my coat.

goat   crow

tin	say	may	day	said	pin
ray	said	win	say	4	3

pin sail do said pin sail say
paid win said say pin said

Side 1

Worksheet

weed rain hill train toad pig

pig	hill	rain
weed	toad	train

u u u u u u u u u u u u

w w w w w w w w w w w

v v v v v v v v v v v

You ate my coat.
You ate my coat.
You ate my coat.

1. sail   2. seal
3. eat   4. mail

Side 2

Worksheet

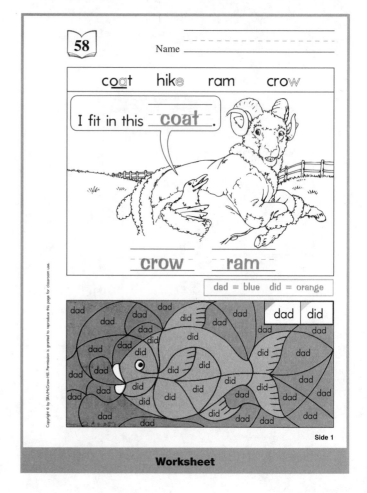

Name

coat   hike   ram   crow

I fit in this _coat_.

crow   ram

dad = blue   did = orange

dad	did

Side 1

Worksheet

32

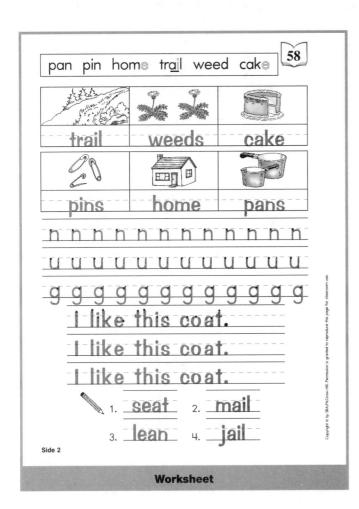

58

pan pin home trail weed cake

trail	weeds	cake
pins	home	pans

n n n n n n n n n n n

u u u u u u u u u u u

g g g g g g g g g g g

I like this coat.

I like this coat.

I like this coat.

1. seat 2. mail

3. lean 4. jail

Side 2

Worksheet

59

Name

hit hike dad fly mile crow

I hate to ___fly___, so I will hike.

crow   dad (or crow)

make fry d̶r̶y̶ lake | make | d̶r̶y̶ |
made day date spy | 4 | 3 |
rake mad d̶r̶y̶ cake made cake
fly make my fry make
take date dig day take day
make mad fly d̶r̶y̶

Side 1

Worksheet

59

nine tree kick path rake snow

snow	path	rake
tree	nine	kick

h h h h h h h h h h h

m m m m m m m m m m m

u u u u u u u u u u u

No more hikes for me.

No more hikes for me.

No more hikes for me.

1. see 2. tree

3. may 4. say

Side 2

Worksheet

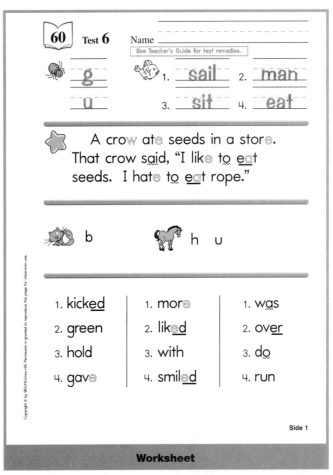

60 Test 6

Name

See Teacher's Guide for test remedies.

g   1. sail 2. man

u   3. sit   4. eat

A crow ate seeds in a store.
That crow said, "I like to eat
seeds. I hate to eat rope."

b   h u

1. kicked	1. more	1. was
2. green	2. liked	2. over
3. hold	3. with	3. do
4. gave	4. smiled	4. run

Side 1

Worksheet

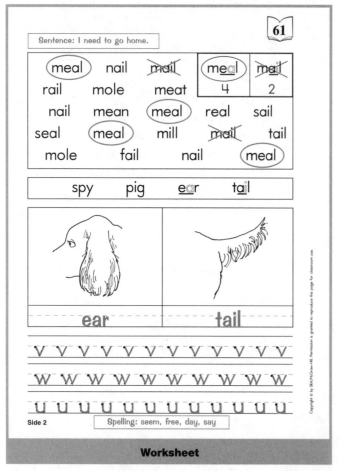

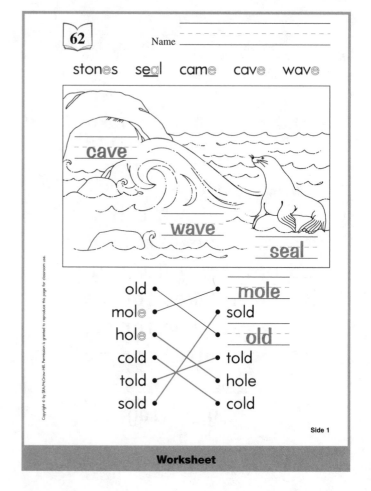

34

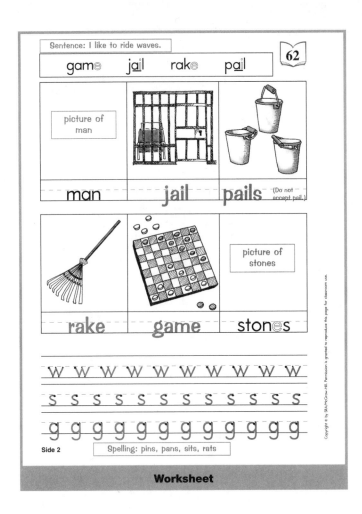

Sentence: I like to ride waves.

62

gam**e**   ja**i**l   rak**e**   pa**i**l

picture of man		
man	jail	pails (Do not accept pail.)

		picture of stones
rake	game	stones

w w w w w w w w w w w

s s s s s s s s s s s

g g g g g g g g g g g

Side 2   Spelling: pins, pans, sits, rats

Worksheet

63

Name _____

t**o**ad   sta**y**   hom**e**   mole

Le**a**ve my **home**.

No. I will **stay**.

Hole Sweet Hole

mole   toad

can   corn   t**ea**r   rams   re**a**d

	picture of rope	
read (or reads)	rop**e**	corn

	picture of tree	
rams	tree	tear

Side 1

Worksheet

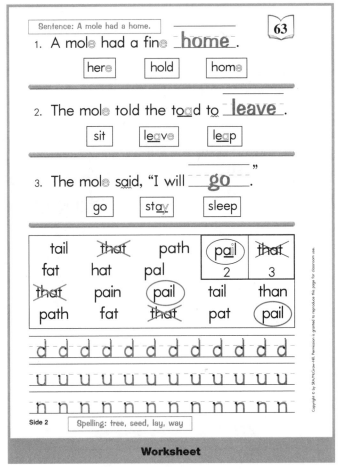

Sentence: A mole had a home.

63

1. A mol**e** had a fin**e** **home**.

   here   hold   hom**e**

2. The mol**e** told the t**o**ad to **leave**.

   sit   l**ea**ve   le**a**p

3. The mol**e** said, "I will **go**."

   go   sta**y**   sleep

tail	~~that~~	path	pail	~~that~~
fat	hat	pal	2	3
~~that~~	pain	pail	tail	than
path	fat	~~that~~	pat	pail

d d d d d d d d d d d d

u u u u u u u u u u u u

n n n n n n n n n n n n

Side 2   Spelling: tree, seed, lay, way

Worksheet

64

Name _____

Fiv**e** cats had fun at a lak**e**.

cat running up hill

cat playing with mole

na**i**l   g**o**at   tree

		picture of smile	
nail	tree	smil**e**	goat

Side 1

Worksheet

35

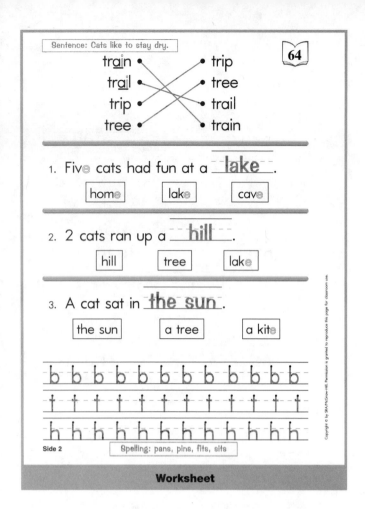

64

Sentence: Cats like to stay dry.

train • • trip
trail • • tree
trip • • trail
tree • • train

1. Five cats had fun at a **lake**.

| home | lake | cave |

2. 2 cats ran up a **hill**.

| hill | tree | lake |

3. A cat sat in **the sun**.

| the sun | a tree | a kite |

b b b b b b b b b b b
t t t t t t t t t t t
h h h h h h h h h h h

Side 2   Spelling: pans, pins, fits, sits

Worksheet

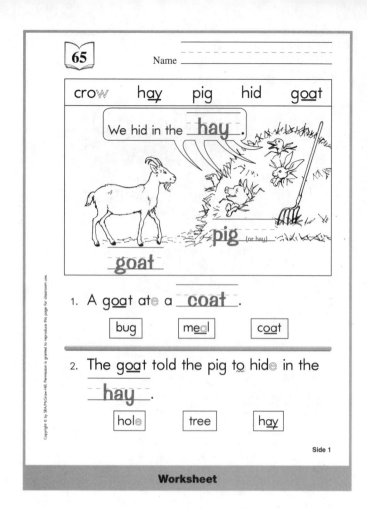

65   Name

crow   hay   pig   hid   goat

We hid in the **hay**.

pig (or hay)

goat

1. A goat ate a **coat**.

| bug | meal | coat |

2. The goat told the pig to hide in the **hay**.

| hole | tree | hay |

Side 1

Worksheet

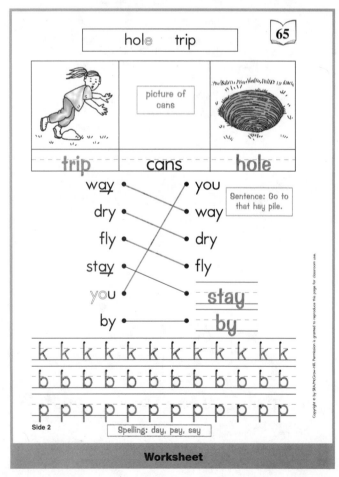

65

hole   trip

| | picture of cans | |

trip   cans   **hole**

way • • you
dry • • way
fly • • dry
stay • • fly
you • **stay**
by • **by**

Sentence: Go to that hay pile.

k k k k k k k k k k k
b b b b b b b b b b b
p p p p p p p p p p p

Side 2   Spelling: day, pay, say

Worksheet

65

The Mole and the Rat

A mole and a rat like to play.

Page 1

Lesson 65
Take Home
The Mole and the Rat

Child folds into a booklet and takes home.

36

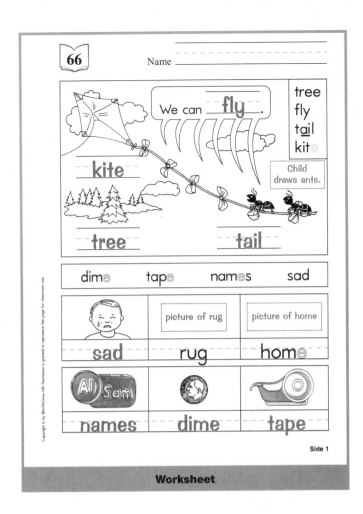

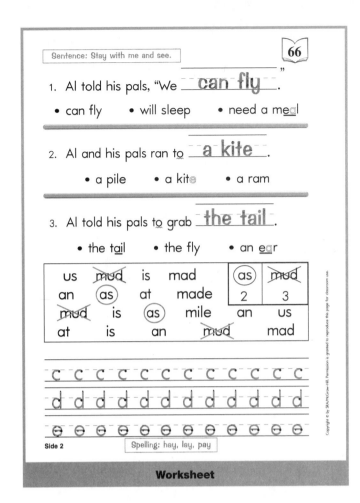

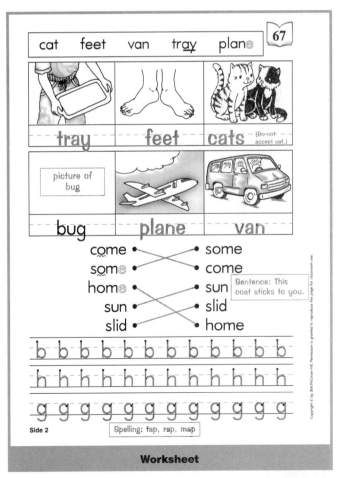

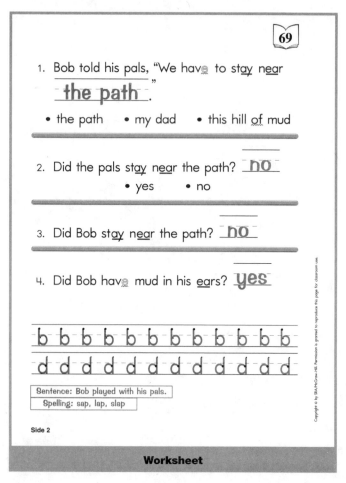

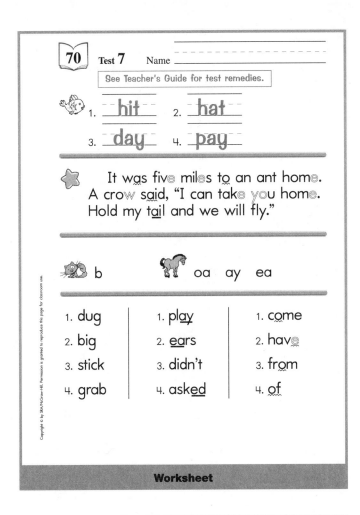

70 Test **7** Name _____

See Teacher's Guide for test remedies.

🐟 1. hit   2. hat

3. day   4. pay

⭐ It was five miles to an ant home.
A crow said, "I can take you home.
Hold my tail and we will fly."

🐭 b   🐴 oa ay ea

1. dug   1. play   1. come
2. big   2. ears   2. have
3. stick   3. didn't   3. from
4. grab   4. asked   4. of

Worksheet

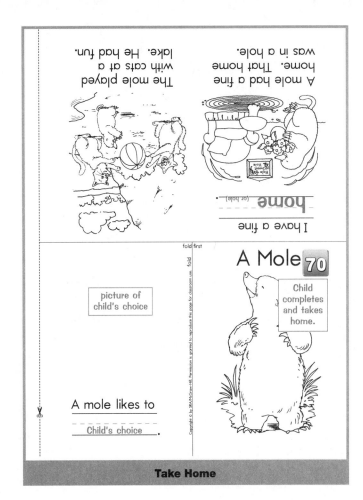

The mole played with cats at a lake. He had fun.

A mole had a fine home. That home was in a hole.

I have a fine home (or hole).

A Mole **70**

Child completes and takes home.

picture of child's choice

fold first
fold

A mole likes to
Child's choice .

Take Home

71 Name _____

1. Bob had to be home by ___ five ___ .
   • 3   • five   • nine

2. A man said, "I see a hill of mud that _____"
   can run
   • can sit   • can eat   • can run

3. Did Bob make it home by five? yes
   • yes   • no

4. Will Bob have to stay at home for some time? yes

5. His dad said, "You didn't stay near the path ."
   • the lake   • the cat   • the path

Side 1

Worksheet

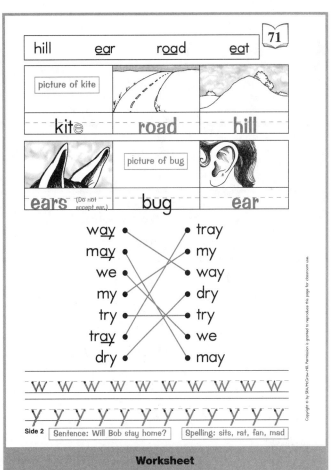

hill   ear   road   eat   **71**

picture of kite

kite   road   hill

ears (Do not accept ear.)   bug   ear

picture of bug

way •   • tray
may •   • my
we •   • way
my •   • dry
try •   • try
tray •   • we
dry •   • may

W W W W W W W W W W W

y y y y y y y y y y y y

Side 2   Sentence: Will Bob stay home?   Spelling: sits, rat, fan, mad

Worksheet

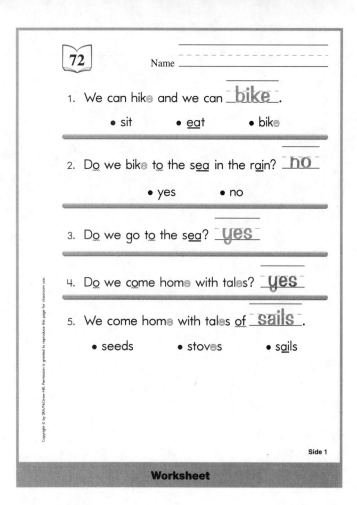

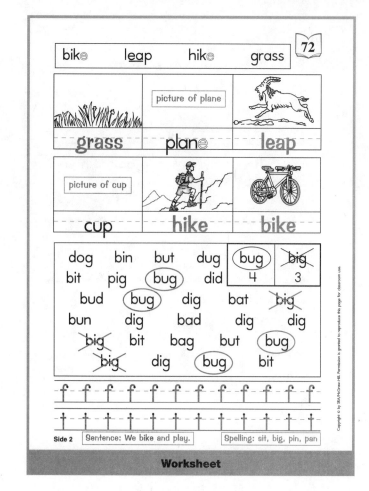

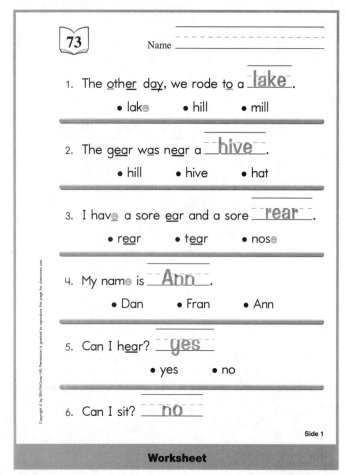

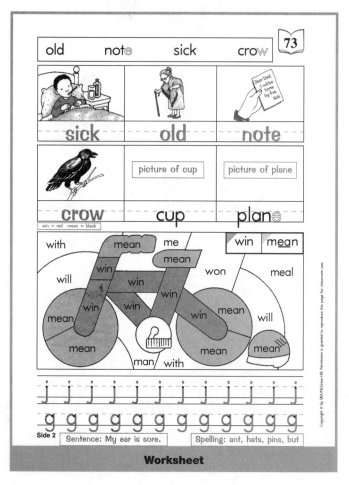

Worksheet 72 — Side 1

Name _____

1. We can hike and we can __bike__.
   • sit   • eat   • bike

2. Do we bike to the sea in the rain? __no__
   • yes   • no

3. Do we go to the sea? __yes__

4. Do we come home with tales? __yes__

5. We come home with tales of __sails__.
   • seeds   • stoves   • sails

Side 1

Worksheet 72 — Side 2

bike   leap   hike   grass

grass   plane   leap

cup   hike   bike

dog bin but dug   bug big
bit pig bug did   4   3
bud bug dig bat big
bun dig bad dig dig
big bit bag but bug
big dig bug bit

Side 2   Sentence: We bike and play.   Spelling: sit, big, pin, pan

Worksheet 73 — Side 1

Name _____

1. The other day, we rode to a __lake__.
   • lake   • hill   • mill

2. The gear was near a __hive__.
   • hill   • hive   • hat

3. I have a sore ear and a sore __rear__.
   • rear   • tear   • nose

4. My name is __Ann__.
   • Dan   • Fran   • Ann

5. Can I hear? __yes__
   • yes   • no

6. Can I sit? __no__

Side 1

Worksheet 73 — Side 2

old   note   sick   crow

sick   old   note

crow   cup   plane

win = red   mean = black

with   mean   me   win   won
will   win   win   meal
win   win
mean   win   mean   will
mean   mean   mean
man   with

win   mean

Side 2   Sentence: My ear is sore.   Spelling: ant, hats, pins, but

40

Worksheet 74 — Side 1

74

Name _____

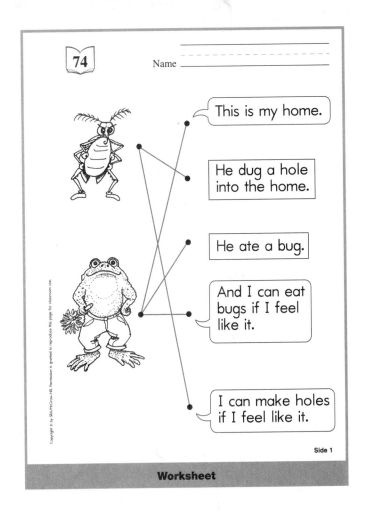

This is my home.

He dug a hole into the home.

He ate a bug.

And I can eat bugs if I feel like it.

I can make holes if I feel like it.

Side 1

Worksheet

Worksheet 74 — Side 2

74

coat   five   run   train   cry

| coats | run (or runs) | train |
| five | coat | cry |

1. Did the toad like holes in his home?

   no   • yes   • no

2. So the toad ___ate the bug___.

   • ate the bug   • ran into a pal
   • sat in the grass

b b b b b b b b b b b b

p p p p p p p p p p p p

Side 2   Sentence: This is my home.   Spelling: ear, heat, eat, near

Worksheet

Worksheet 75 — Side 1

75

Name _____

1. I have to sit in ___the rain___.

   • my home   • a lake   • the rain

2. I wait for ___my pal___.

   • a cat   • my pal   • the sun

3. Is my pal late? ___yes___

   • yes   • no

4. Do I see him at last? ___yes___

5. Will we have fun? ___yes___

Side 1

Worksheet

Worksheet 75 — Side 2

75

stone   trail   pigs   fan   pile   cave

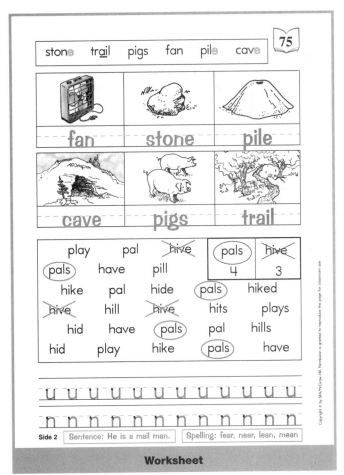

| fan | stone | pile |
| cave | pigs | trail |

play	pal	~~hive~~	pals	~~hive~~
pals	have	pill	4	3
hike	pal	~~hide~~	pals	hiked
~~hive~~	hill	~~hive~~	hits	plays
hid	have	pals	pal	hills
hid	play	hike	pals	have

u u u u u u u u u u u u

n n n n n n n n n n n n

Side 2   Sentence: He is a mail man.   Spelling: fear, near, lean, mean

Worksheet

Dad, can I go for a hike with my pals?

Child completes and takes home.

Bob

Page 2

Lesson 75
Take Home
Bob, The Hill of Mud

Yes, Bob, you may go. But you have to stay near the path. And you have to come home by five.

Child completes and takes home.

dad

Page 3

Lesson 75
Take Home
Bob, The Hill of Mud

76 Name _____

1. We played with __a stick__ .
   • a stick   • a mole   • a dime

2. We played in __the rain__ .
   • his home   • the rain   • the sun

3. Did we eat near the stove? __yes__
   • yes   • no

4. I go to the __rug__ .
   • sun   • rug   • lake

5. Is it time for me to sleep? __yes__

Side 1

Worksheet

76

| train | jump | slap | weed |

picture of tree

tree   jump (or jumps)   weed (or weeds)

slap (or slaps)   train   home

have   hate   (other)   (other)   have
over   hay   has   3   4
the   have   has   of   hive   the
(other)   have   hike   over   hay
hate   (other)   have   over

k k k k k k k k k k k k

e e e e e e e e e e e e e

Side 2   Sentence: At last I was dry.   Spelling: ears, fears, tears, learn

Worksheet

Worksheet 77 — Side 1

Name _____

We must keep that fire from __the   barn__ .

bad
the
big
b<u>a</u>rn

I will make that fire __big__ .

1. Who made the pals cold?   __a wind__
   • a pig   • a wind   • a cat

2. Who made a fire?   __the pals__
   • the pals   • the wind   • my dad

3. Did the fire get big?   __yes__
   • yes   • no

Side 1

Worksheet

Worksheet 77 — Side 2

spy   math   rake   p<u>a</u>rk   s<u>oa</u>ked   hive

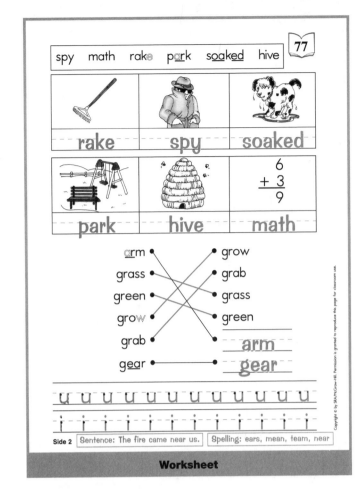

| rake | spy | soaked |
| park | hive | math |

$$\begin{array}{r} 6 \\ + 3 \\ \hline 9 \end{array}$$

<u>a</u>rm • — • grow
grass • — • grab
green • — • grass
grow • — • green
grab •
g<u>ea</u>r • — • __arm__
               __gear__

u u u u u u u u u u u u

i i i i i i i i i i i i

Side 2   Sentence: The fire came near us.   Spelling: ears, mean, team, near

Worksheet

Worksheet 78 — Side 1

Name _____

fire   b<u>a</u>rn   pals

Ho ho. It's time for a __barn   fire__ .

__barn__
__pals__   __fire__

c<u>a</u>r   g<u>ea</u>r   seeds   sky

| gear | seeds | car | sky |

Side 1

Worksheet

Worksheet 78 — Side 2

1. Who made a bad joke?   __the wind__
   • Bob   • the pals   • the wind

2. Who made the fire lick at the b<u>a</u>rn?
   __the wind__
   • the wind   • the pals   • Bob

3. Will the pals save the b<u>a</u>rn?
   __Child's choice__
   • yes   • no   • I don't know.

w<u>o</u>n • — • __come__
so • — • won
come • — • some
came • — • so
some • — • came

k k k k k k k k k k k k

y y y y y y y y y y y y

Side 2   Sentence: Flames are near the barn.   Spelling: ar, farm, bar, art, arm

Worksheet

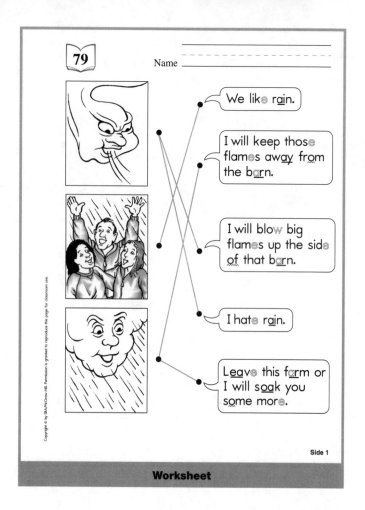

79 Name _____

We like rain.

I will keep those flames away from the barn.

I will blow big flames up the side of that barn.

I hate rain.

Leave this farm or I will soak you some more.

Side 1

Worksheet

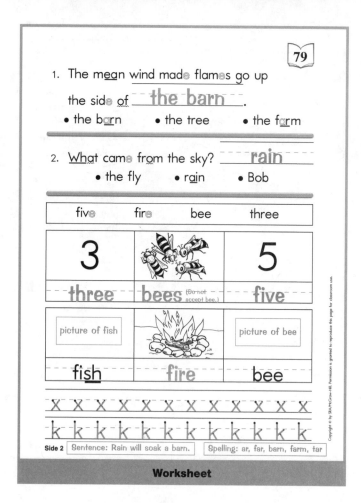

79

1. The mean wind made flames go up the side of _____the barn_____.
   • the barn   • the tree   • the farm

2. What came from the sky? _____rain_____
   • the fly   • rain   • Bob

five	fire	bee	three

three | bees (Do not accept bee.) | five
fish | fire | bee

X X X X X X X X X X X X

k k k k k k k k k k k k

Side 2 | Sentence: Rain will soak a barn. | Spelling: ar, far, barn, farm, tar

Worksheet

80 Test **8** Name _____

See Teacher's Guide for test remedies.

1. far   2. fan
3. farm   4. pin

Ann and some pals rode bikes to a lake. The pals played games and ate. No hive was near the gear, so Ann is fine.

wh   sh   ar

1. jump   1. hill   1. are
2. don't   2. barn   2. who
3. wind   3. while   3. other
4. dive   4. began   4. you

Worksheet

At last my pal is home. We have fun as we play with a stick and play in the rain.

I hear him and see him. I will jump up. It's time for us to have some fun.

fold first

My Pal

Child folds and takes home.

It is time to eat. We will eat in his home near the stove. At last I am dry. It is time for me to sleep.

I hate to wait. But I have to sit and wait while it rains.

Take Home

44

81

Name

I have a rug.

I don't like mud.

This rug is fast.

We can sit on the rug.

f f f f f f f f f f f f

X X X X X X X X X X X

Side 1

Worksheet

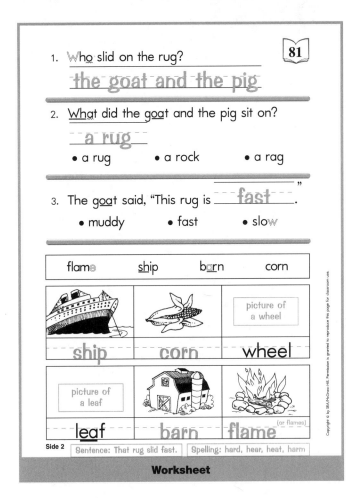

81

1. Who slid on the rug?

the goat and the pig

2. What did the goat and the pig sit on?

a rug
- a rug
- a rock
- a rag

3. The goat said, "This rug is ___fast___."
- muddy
- fast
- slow

flame	ship	barn	corn

		picture of a wheel
ship	corn	wheel

picture of a leaf		(or flames)
leaf	barn	flame

Side 2 | Sentence: That rug slid fast. | Spelling: hard, hear, heat, harm |

Worksheet

82

Name

A tree is in the way.

We will miss that tree.

We can slide on the mud some more.

The goat and I have mud on us.

X X X X X X X X X X X

h h h h h h h h h h h h h

Side 1

Worksheet

82

1. What did the pals land in?

mud
- tree
- grass
- mud

2. What did the rug run into? ___a tree___
- a rug
- a rock
- a tree

3. Who said, "We can slide on the mud some more"? ___the goat___
- the goat
- the pig
- the ram

crow	bee	loaf	plane	sky

picture of a sun		
sun	bees (Do not accept bee.)	sky

loaf	crow	plane

Side 2 | Sentence: We will slide some more. | Spelling: heat, hard, far, fear |

Worksheet

45

83

Name _____

tree   you   mole   fun   some   crow

I will have **some fun** .

crow

Who **are** **you** ?

tree

mole

Side 1

Worksheet

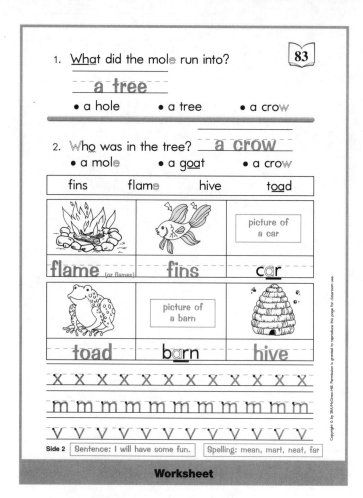

83

1. What did the mole run into?   **a tree**
   • a hole   • a tree   • a crow

2. Who was in the tree?   **a crow**
   • a mole   • a goat   • a crow

fins	flame	hive	toad

flame (or flames)	**fins**	**car**
toad	**barn**	**hive**

X X X X X X X X X X X X

m m m m m m m m m m m m m

V V V V V V V V V V V V

Side 2   Sentence: I will have some fun.   Spelling: mean, mart, neat, far

Worksheet

84

Name _____

feet   crow   free   home

You dug into the side of my **home** .

I need to free thes**e** **feet** .

1. Who told the mole **what** to do?   **the crow**
   • the tree   • the snake   • the crow

2. The mole said, "I dig, dig, dig, but these feet **are**
   big, big, big "
   • old, old, old   • deep   • big, big, big

3. A mole came to the home of a wise **snake** .
   • duck   • snake   • man

Side 1

Worksheet

84

asked • ——— • **sailed**
began • ——— • sail
sailed • ——— • **ask**
ask • ——— • asked
sail • ——— • began

none	one	two	three	five	nine

9	‖‖‖‖‖	‖‖
nine	**five**	**two**
‖		**3**
one	**none**	**three**

X X X X X X X X X X X X

a a a a a a a a a a a a

y y y y y y y y y y y y

Side 2   Sentence: The mole dug a hole.   Spelling: boat, lean, loan, barn

Worksheet

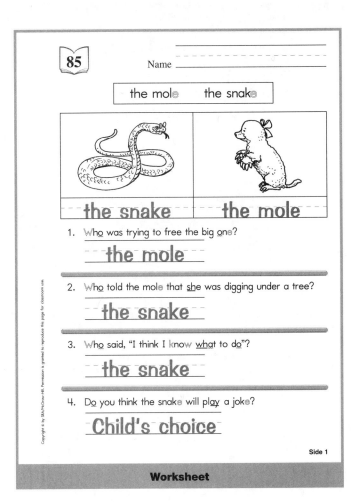

85

Name _____

the mole   the snake

the snake	the mole

1. Who was trying to free the big one?

   the mole

2. Who told the mole that she was digging under a tree?

   the snake

3. Who said, "I think I know what to do"?

   the snake

4. Do you think the snake will play a joke?

   Child's choice

Side 1

Worksheet

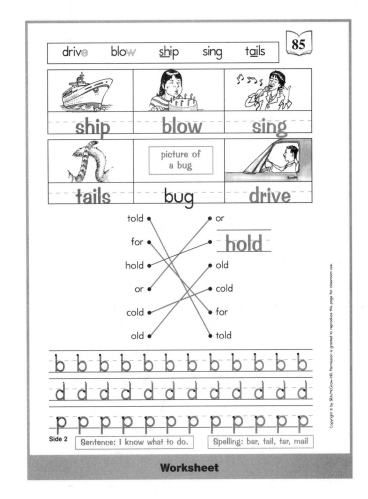

85

drive   blow   ship   sing   tails

ship	blow	sing
tails	bug	drive

told •   • or
for •   • **hold**
hold •   • old
or •   • cold
cold •   • for
old •   • told

b b b b b b b b b b b

d d d d d d d d d d d

p p p p p p p p p p p

Side 2   Sentence: I know what to do.   Spelling: bar, tail, tar, mail

Worksheet

I have a sore ear, but I can hear. And I have a

____ **sore** ____ rear. So I can't sit. And I can't ride my bike for a while.

From Ann

Child completes and takes home.

Page 4

Lesson 85
Take Home
Note to Dad

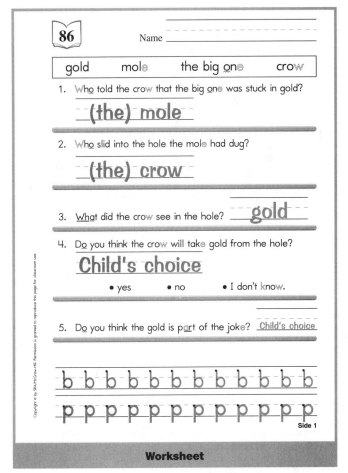

86

Name _____

gold   mole   the big one   crow

1. Who told the crow that the big one was stuck in gold?

   (the) mole

2. Who slid into the hole the mole had dug?

   (the) crow

3. What did the crow see in the hole?   **gold**

4. Do you think the crow will take gold from the hole?

   Child's choice

   • yes   • no   • I don't know.

5. Do you think the gold is part of the joke?   _Child's choice_

b b b b b b b b b b b

p p p p p p p p p p p

Side 1

Worksheet

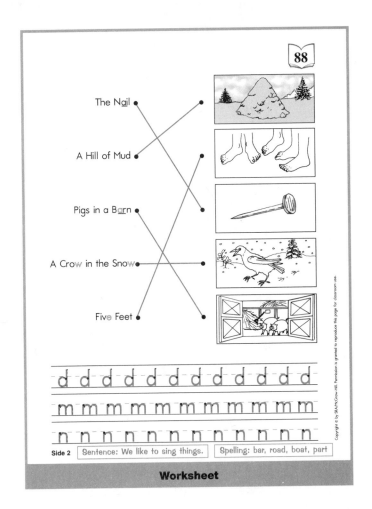

The N<u>ai</u>l

A Hill of Mud

Pigs in a B<u>ar</u>n

A Cr<u>ow</u> in the Snow

Five F<u>ee</u>t

d d d d d d d d d d d d

m m m m m m m m m m m m

n n n n n n n n n n n n

Side 2 | Sentence: We like to sing things. | Spelling: bar, road, boat, part

Worksheet

pig   corn   goat   cow

pig

cow

goat   pil<u>e</u> of **corn**

1. <u>What</u> did the pig and the g<u>oa</u>t like to d<u>o</u>? ___**eat**___
   • sit   • eat   • sleep

2. Wh<u>o</u> told the pig and the g<u>oa</u>t to st<u>ar</u>t eating?
   a cow   • Bob   • a crow   • a cow

3. Wh<u>o</u> <u>a</u>te faster? **(the) a cow**

Side 1

Worksheet

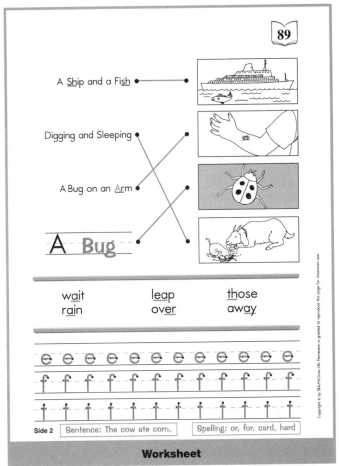

A <u>Sh</u>ip and a Fi<u>sh</u>

Digging and Sleeping

A Bug on an <u>Ar</u>m

A Bug

| w<u>ai</u>t | l<u>ea</u>p | <u>th</u>ose |
| r<u>ai</u>n | <u>o</u>ver | away |

e e e e e e e e e e e e

f f f f f f f f f f f f

t t t t t t t t t t t t

Side 2 | Sentence: The cow ate corn. | Spelling: or, for, card, hard

Worksheet

90 Test **9**   Name

See Teacher's Guide for test remedies.

1. **bar**   2. **told**   3. **hard**

One d<u>ay</u>, a g<u>oa</u>t and a pig w<u>ere</u> pl<u>ay</u>ing n<u>ear</u> a pil<u>e</u> of corn.
The g<u>oa</u>t said, "I can eat that corn."
The pig said, "Me too."

o   er

1. <u>she</u>	1. got	1. said
2. w<u>ere</u>	2. think	2. was
3. st<u>ar</u>ted	3. now	3. <u>what</u>
4. pl<u>ay</u>ing	4. und<u>er</u>	4. gold

Worksheet

49

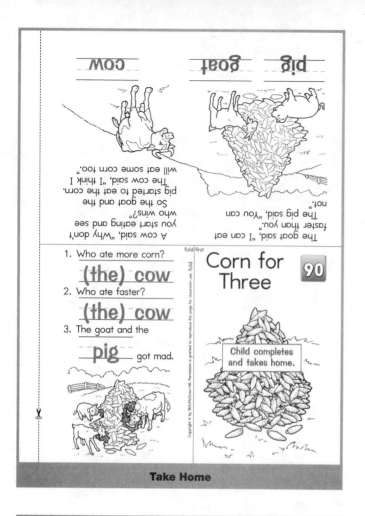

Take Home

Corn for Three **90**

(the image shows the upside-down portion "Corn for Three" fold-out, with text:)

The goat said, "I can eat faster than you." The pig said, "You can not."

A cow said, "Why don't you start eating and see who wins?" So the goat and the pig started to eat the corn. The cow said, "I think I will eat some corn too."

1. Who ate more corn? **(the) cow**

2. Who ate faster? **(the) cow**

3. The goat and the **pig** got mad.

Child completes and takes home.

I **wait** for my **pal**.

rain
pal
hate
wait

1. Did the sun shine? **no**

2. What parts were soaked? **coat and tail**
   - coat and hat
   - coat and tail
   - tail and mail

3. What did the pals plan to do? **have lots of fun**
   - have a meal
   - have some gum
   - have lots of fun

4. Who is the pal? **the mail man**
   - the dog
   - the mail man
   - Bob

Side 1

Worksheet

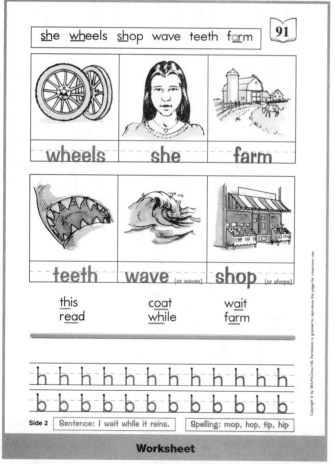

91

she wheels shop wave teeth farm

wheels   she   farm

teeth   wave (or waves)   shop (or shops)

this   coat   wait
read   while   farm

h h h h h h h h h h h h h h h
b b b b b b b b b b b b b b b

Side 2   Sentence: I wait while it rains.   Spelling: mop, hop, tip, hip

Worksheet

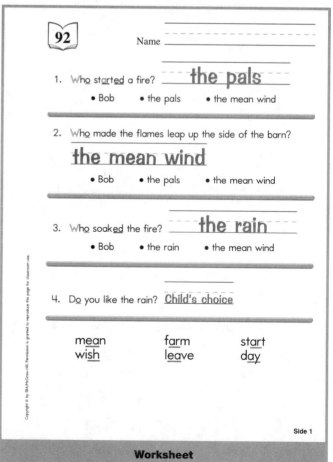

1. Who started a fire? **the pals**
   - Bob
   - the pals
   - the mean wind

2. Who made the flames leap up the side of the barn? **the mean wind**
   - Bob
   - the pals
   - the mean wind

3. Who soaked the fire? **the rain**
   - Bob
   - the rain
   - the mean wind

4. Do you like the rain? **Child's choice**

mean   farm   start
wish   leave   day

Side 1

Worksheet

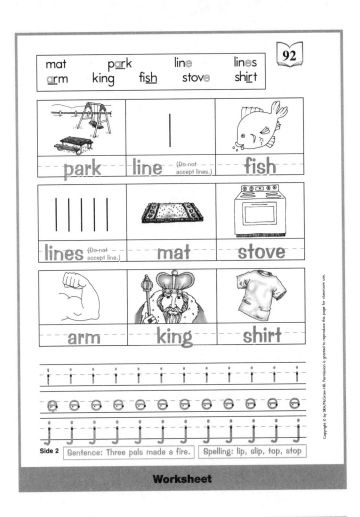

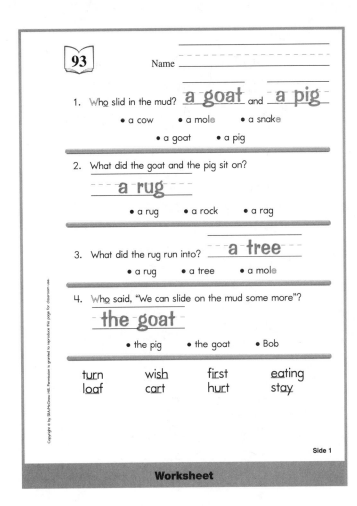

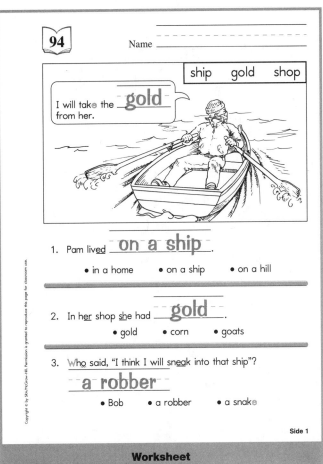

c<u>ar</u>   folding   h<u>ur</u>t   cop   b<u>ir</u>d   ca<u>sh</u>

bird   hurt   cash

folding   cop   car

over • — • mother
under • — • her
other • — • here
mother • — • other
here • — • over
her • — • under

j j j j j j j j j j j j j j j

p p p p p p p p p p p p p p p

g g g g g g g g g g g g g g g

Side 2 | Sentence: Pam made rings and things. | Spelling: rip, trip, top, stop

Worksheet

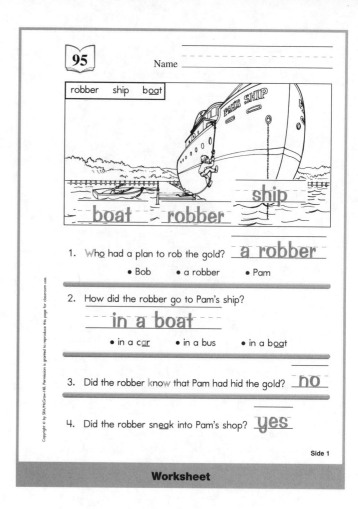

Name _____

robber   ship   b<u>oa</u>t

PAMS SHIP

boat   robber   ship

1. W<u>h</u>o had a plan to rob the gold?   a robber
   • Bob   • a robber   • Pam

2. How did the robber go to Pam's ship?
   in a boat
   • in a c<u>ar</u>   • in a bus   • in a b<u>oa</u>t

3. Did the robber <u>k</u>now that Pam had hid the gold?   no

4. Did the robber sn<u>ea</u>k into Pam's shop?   yes

Side 1

Worksheet

sack   b<u>ur</u>n   slid<u>e</u>   c<u>ar</u>d   cop   rocks

burn   sack   cop

slide   rocks   card

ships   boat   first
play   sneak   were
und<u>er</u>   dark   whil<u>e</u>

k k k k k k k k k k k k k

m m m m m m m m m m m m m

y y y y y y y y y y y y y

Side 2 | Sentence: She hid her gold. | Spelling: rip, grip, trip, drip

Worksheet

Child folds into a booklet and takes home.

What Jan Sings

Jan liked to sing, but she made her mother sick of her singing.

Page 1

Lesson 95
Take Home
What Jan Sings

Name

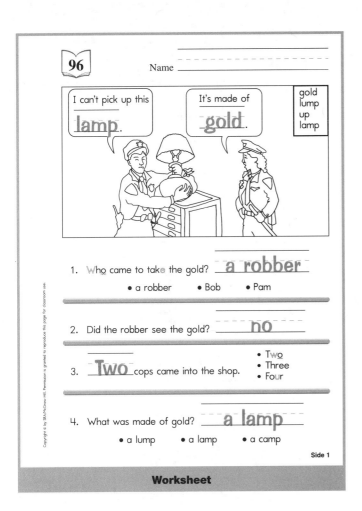

I can't pick up this **lamp**.

It's made of **gold**.

gold
lump
up
lamp

1. Who came to take the gold? **a robber**
   • a robber   • Bob   • Pam

2. Did the robber see the gold? **no**

3. **Two** cops came into the shop.
   • Two
   • Three
   • Four

4. What was made of gold? **a lamp**
   • a lump   • a lamp   • a camp

Side 1

Worksheet

shirt   teeth   hat   clock   corn   barking

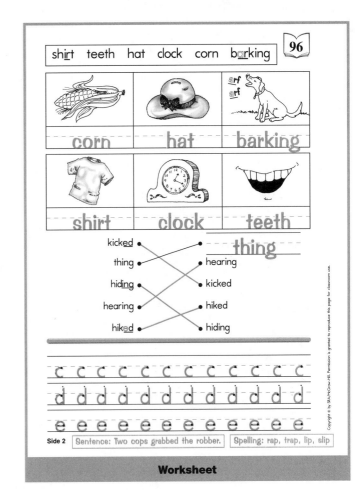

corn   hat   barking

shirt   clock   teeth

kicked   **thing**
thing   hearing
hiding   kicked
hearing   hiked
hiked   hiding

c c c c c c c c c c c c
d d d d d d d d d d d d
e e e e e e e e e e e e

Side 2 | Sentence: Two cops grabbed the robber. | | Spelling: rap, trap, lip, slip |

Worksheet

Name

What I sing will **bring rain**.

rain so bring

I don't think **so**.

mother   dirt   Sid   clean

1. Who liked things that were clean? **Sid**

2. The town had lots **of dirt**.
   • of dirt   • of trees   • of grass

3. Who said, "I will sing to make it rain"? **Sid**

4. Who said, "Singing will not make it rain"?
   mother

Side 1

Worksheet

sack   running   butter   sitting   rings

running   sack   butter

picture of a
fly or
something
flying

sitting   rings   fly

starter   ear   raining   cash
later   barking   away   sailed

o o o o o o o o o o o o
a a a a a a a a a a a a
r r r r r r r r r r r r

Side 2 | Sentence: He made things clean. | | Spelling: not, got, hit, bit |

Worksheet

53

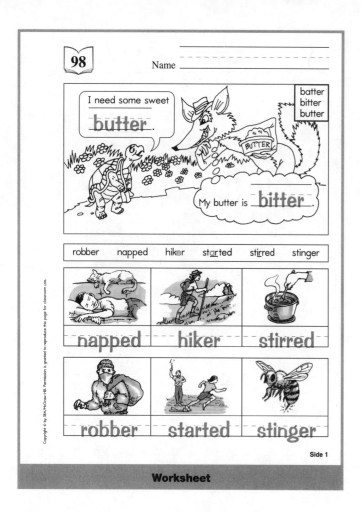

98 Name _____

I need some sweet **butter**.

batter
bitter
butter

My butter is **bitter**.

| robber | napped | hiker | started | stirred | stinger |

napped **hiker** **stirred**

robber **started** **stinger**

Side 1

Worksheet

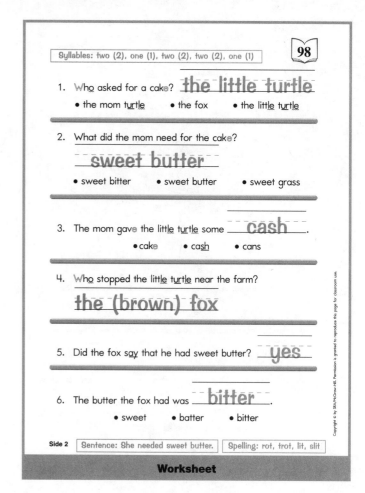

Syllables: two (2), one (1), two (2), two (2), one (1)

1. Who asked for a cake?   **the little turtle**
   • the mom turtle   • the fox   • the little turtle

2. What did the mom need for the cake?
   sweet butter
   • sweet bitter   • sweet butter   • sweet grass

3. The mom gave the little turtle some ___**cash**___.
   • cake   • cash   • cans

4. Who stopped the little turtle near the farm?
   the (brown) fox

5. Did the fox say that he had sweet butter?   **yes**

6. The butter the fox had was ___**bitter**___.
   • sweet   • batter   • bitter

Side 2 | Sentence: She needed sweet butter. | | Spelling: rot, trot, lit, slit |

Worksheet

99 Name _____

Can I **taste** that cake?

cake
taste
mom

cake

mom

| town | ship | darts | barn | clock | cold |

ship **barn** **cold**

darts **clock** **town**

Side 1

Worksheet

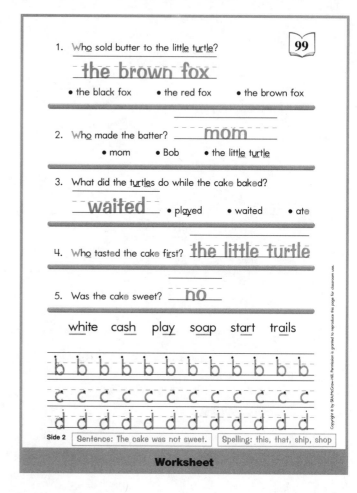

1. Who sold butter to the little turtle?
   the brown fox
   • the black fox   • the red fox   • the brown fox

2. Who made the batter?   **mom**
   • mom   • Bob   • the little turtle

3. What did the turtles do while the cake baked?
   waited   • played   • waited   • ate

4. Who tasted the cake first?   **the little turtle**

5. Was the cake sweet?   **no**

white   cash   play   soap   start   trails

b b b b b b b b b b b b b

c c c c c c c c c c c c c

d d d d d d d d d d d d d

Side 2 | Sentence: The cake was not sweet. | | Spelling: this, that, ship, shop |

Worksheet

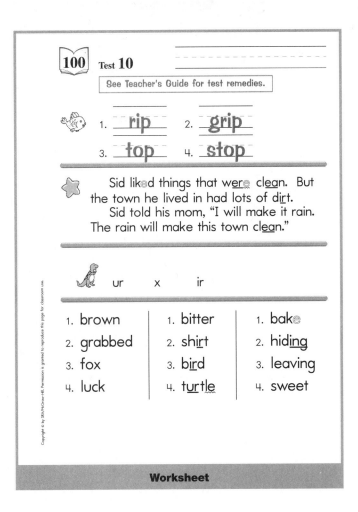

Page 100 — Test 10

See Teacher's Guide for test remedies.

1. rip   2. grip
3. top   4. stop

Sid liked things that were clean. But the town he lived in had lots of dirt. Sid told his mom, "I will make it rain. The rain will make this town clean."

ur	x	ir
1. brown	1. bitter	1. bake
2. grabbed	2. shirt	2. hiding
3. fox	3. bird	3. leaving
4. luck	4. turtle	4. sweet

Worksheet

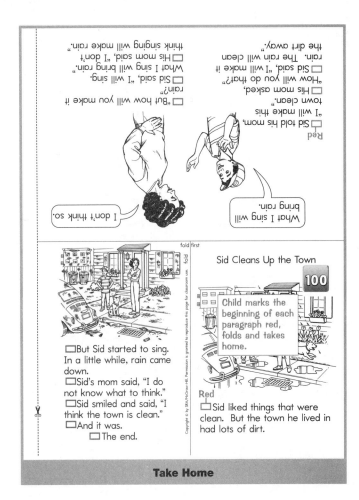

Take Home

"But how will you make it rain?"

☐ Sid said, "I will sing."
☐ What I sing will bring rain.
☐ His mom said, "I don't think singing will make rain."

Red
☐ Sid told his mom, "I will make this town clean."
☐ "How will you do that?" His mom asked.
☐ Sid said, "I will make it rain. The rain will clean the dirt away."

What I sing will bring rain.

I don't think so.

Sid Cleans Up the Town

100

Child marks the beginning of each paragraph red, folds and takes home.

fold first

fold

Red
☐ Sid liked things that were clean. But the town he lived in had lots of dirt.

☐ But Sid started to sing. In a little while, rain came down.
☐ Sid's mom said, "I do not know what to think."
☐ Sid smiled and said, "I think the town is clean."
☐ And it was.
☐ The end.

101

Name

Who sold you this **butter**?

fox
cake
butter

The **fox**.

hill   farm   seat   arms   cake   hot

arms   cake   farm

hill   seat(or seats)   hot

Side 1

Worksheet

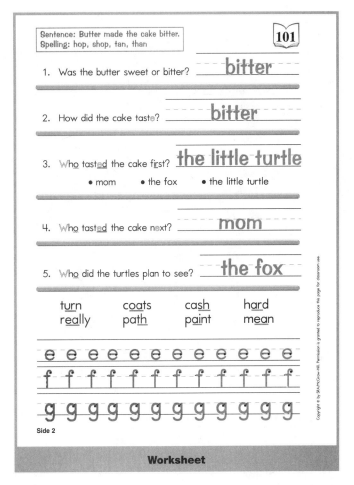

101

Sentence: Butter made the cake bitter.
Spelling: hop, shop, tan, than

1. Was the butter sweet or bitter? ___ **bitter**

2. How did the cake taste? ___ **bitter**

3. Who tasted the cake first? ___ **the little turtle**
   • mom   • the fox   • the little turtle

4. Who tasted the cake next? ___ **mom**

5. Who did the turtles plan to see? ___ **the fox**

turn   coats   cash   hard
really   path   paint   mean

e e e e e e e e e e e e
f f f f f f f f f f f f
g g g g g g g g g g g g

Side 2

Worksheet

55

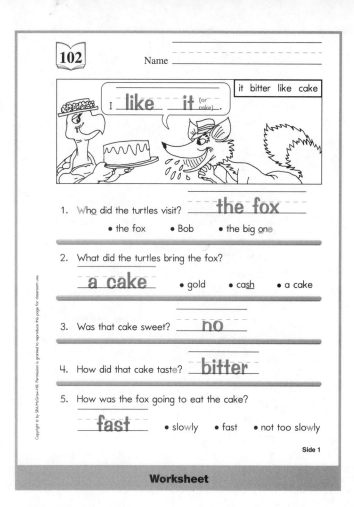

102   Name _____

I **like** **it** (or cake).

it bitter like cake

1. Who did the turtles visit? **the fox**
   • the fox   • Bob   • the big one

2. What did the turtles bring the fox?
   a cake   • gold   • cash   • a cake

3. Was that cake sweet? **no**

4. How did that cake taste? **bitter**

5. How was the fox going to eat the cake?
   fast   • slowly   • fast   • not too slowly

Side 1

Worksheet

102

| cash | soaked | pond | rocks | box | chair |

box   cash   rocks

chair   pond   soaked

over   maybe   dirty
chase   card   shame
train   throw   away

Sentence: The turtles visited the fox.

h h h h h h h h h h h h h
i i i i i i i i i i i i i
j j j j j j j j j j j j j

Side 2   Spelling: fun, sun, thin, pin

Worksheet

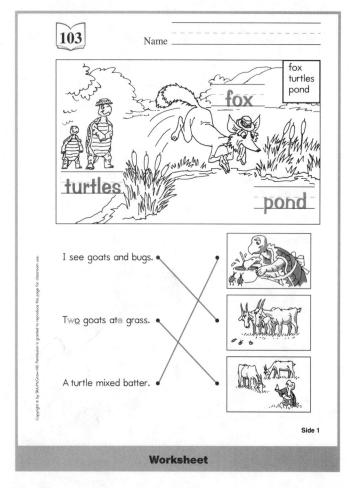

103   Name _____

fox
turtles
pond

fox

turtles

pond

I see goats and bugs.

Two goats ate grass.

A turtle mixed batter.

Side 1

Worksheet

103

1. Who ate the cake? **the fox**
   • the fox   • Bob   • the big one

2. How did the cake taste? **bitter** (or bad)

3. After the fox ate the cake, he said, "I need something
   to drink."
   • to eat   • to see   • to drink

4. He ran to the **pond**.   • town   • pond   • farm

5. Did he dive in? **yes**

Sentence: It did not go away.

6. Did the cake leave a bad taste? **yes**

k k k k k k k k k k k k
m m m m m m m m m m m m
n n n n n n n n n n n n

Side 2   Spelling: not, nut, shut, shot

Worksheet

Name _____

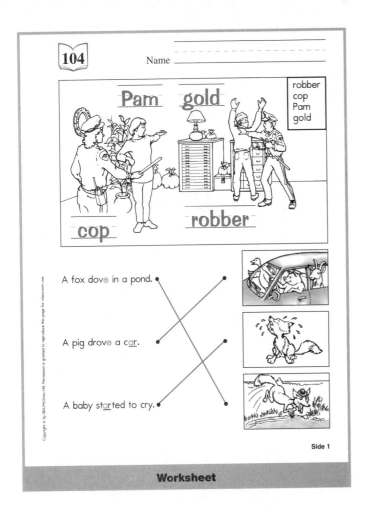

Pam	gold
cop	robber

robber
cop
Pam
gold

A fox dove in a pond. •

A pig drove a car. •

A baby started to cry. •

Side 1

Worksheet

1. Pam's shop was in her ___**ship**___.
   • car   • ship   • boat

2. Who had a plan to take her gold? **the robber**
   • Bob   • the robber   • two cops

3. How did the robber go to Pam's ship?   • in a car
   in a boat   • in a boat
   • in a truck

4. Did the robber think the gold was in a lump? **yes**

5. Who grabbed the robber? **two cops**

6. Pam made the gold into **a lamp**   • a lump
   • a bar
   • a lamp

Sentence: Why are you happy?

V V V V V V V V V V V V V

X X X X X X X X X X X X X

Y Y Y Y Y Y Y Y Y Y Y Y Y

Side 2   Spelling: but, bit, hit, hut

Worksheet

Name _____

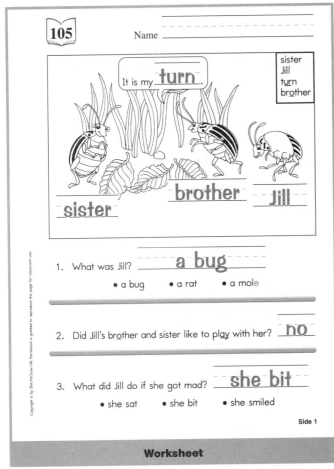

It is my **turn**.

sister
Jill
turn
brother

brother   Jill

sister

1. What was Jill? ___**a bug**___
   • a bug   • a rat   • a mole

2. Did Jill's brother and sister like to play with her? **no**

3. What did Jill do if she got mad? **she bit**
   • she sat   • she bit   • she smiled

Side 1

Worksheet

Sentence: It is not her turn.

4. One day, Jill was playing with her brother and
   ___**her sister**___.
   • her mother   • her dad   • her sister

5. Who did Jill bite? **her brother**
   • her mother   • her brother   • her sister

hiding	hunt	hot	throw	town	dirt

hiding   throw   dirt

town   hot   hunt

Side 2   Spelling: boat, bait, raid, road

Worksheet

57

___ robber

Child completes and takes home.

A robber got into her shop to take the gold.

He said, "I see sacks and rocks and clocks. And I see a big lamp. But I see no gold."

Page 2

**Lesson 105
Take Home
How Pam Hid Her Gold**

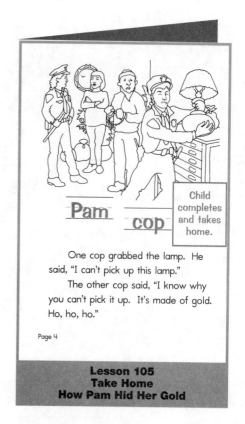

Pam ___ ___ cop

Child completes and takes home.

One cop grabbed the lamp. He said, "I can't pick up this lamp."

The other cop said, "I know why you can't pick it up. It's made of gold. Ho, ho, ho."

Page 4

**Lesson 105
Take Home
How Pam Hid Her Gold**

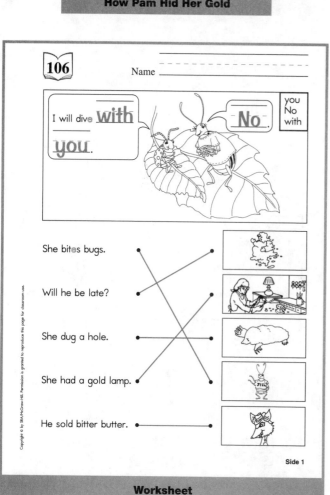

106

Name _____

I will dive **with** **you** .

No .

you No with

She bites bugs.

Will he be late?

She dug a hole.

She had a gold lamp.

He sold bitter butter.

Side 1

Worksheet

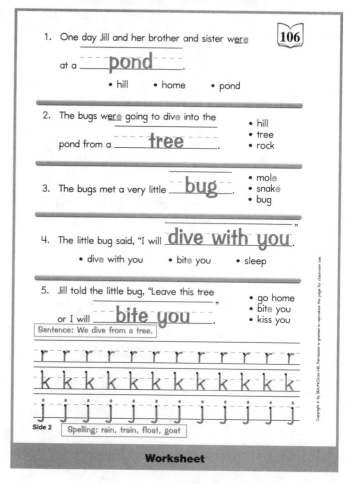

106

1. One day Jill and her brother and sister were at a ___ **pond** ___ .
   • hill   • home   • pond

2. The bugs were going to dive into the pond from a ___ **tree** ___ .
   • hill
   • tree
   • rock

3. The bugs met a very little ___ **bug** .
   • mole
   • snake
   • bug

4. The little bug said, "I will **dive with you** ."
   • dive with you   • bite you   • sleep

5. Jill told the little bug, "Leave this tree ___ " or I will **bite you** ___ .
   • go home
   • bite you
   • kiss you

Sentence: We dive from a tree.
_____

r r r r r r r r r r r r r

k k k k k k k k k k k k k

j j j j j j j j j j j j j

Side 2   Spelling: rain, train, float, goat

Worksheet

58

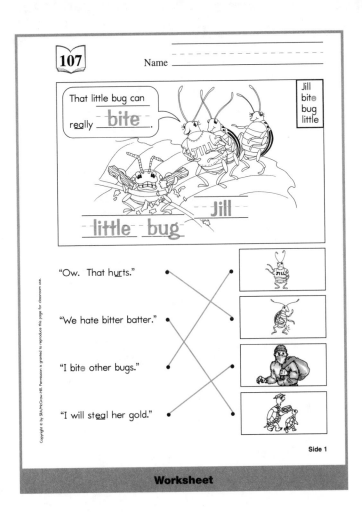

107   Name _____

That little bug can really __bite__ .

Jill
bite
bug
little

__Jill__
__little__ __bug__

"Ow. That hurts."

"We hate bitter batter."

"I bite other bugs."

"I will steal her gold."

Side 1

Worksheet

107

1. The little bug said, "I can __bite hard__ ."
   • bite hard   • swim fast   • eat leaves

2. Who said, "You can't beat me at biting"?
   __Jill__

3. Jill bit a __stick__ .
   • bug
   • leaf
   • stick

4. Who broke a stick? __the little bug__
   • Jill   • the little bug   • Bob

5. The little bug bit a bigger stick and __broke it__
   • made a mark
   • broke it
   • made no mark

Sentence: That bug is really tiny.

o o o o o o o o o o o o
r r r r r r r r r r r r
p p p p p p p p p p p p

Side 2   Spelling: loaf, leaf, read, road

Worksheet

108   Name _____

fishing   swimming   diving   hiking   sun

Later we can go __Child's choice__

__sun__

~~those~~	this	that	(these)	(thes**e**)	~~those~~
that	the	three	this	3	4
teeth	the	~~those~~	than	(these)
that	throw	the	than	that
~~those~~	that	thank	thin	~~those~~
that	the	thin	(these)	thank

Side 1

Worksheet

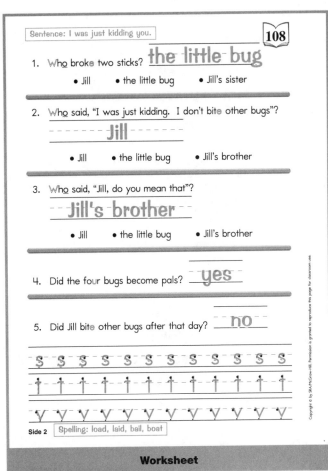

Sentence: I was just kidding you.   **108**

1. Who broke two sticks? __the little bug__
   • Jill   • the little bug   • Jill's sister

2. Who said, "I was just kidding. I don't bite other bugs"?
   __Jill__
   • Jill   • the little bug   • Jill's brother

3. Who said, "Jill, do you mean that"?
   __Jill's brother__
   • Jill   • the little bug   • Jill's brother

4. Did the four bugs become pals? __yes__

5. Did Jill bite other bugs after that day? __no__

S S S S S S S S S S S S
t t t t t t t t t t t t
v v v v v v v v v v v v

Side 2   Spelling: load, laid, bail, boat

Worksheet

59

109

Name _____

Row, __row__,
__row__, the boat.

Rain, __rain__,
clean __this__
__town__.

baby	shirt	winter	summer

__shirt__ | __winter__ | __pants__

picture of a hat | |

__hat__ | __baby__ | __summer__

Side 1

Worksheet

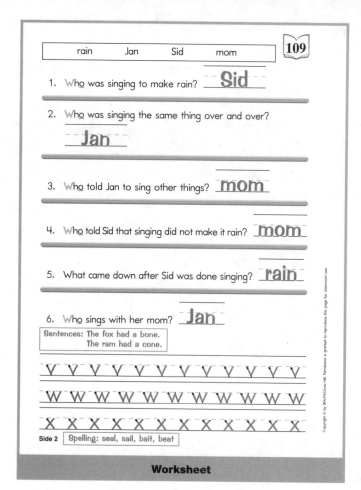

109

rain	Jan	Sid	mom

1. Who was singing to make rain? __Sid__

2. Who was singing the same thing over and over?
__Jan__

3. Who told Jan to sing other things? __mom__

4. Who told Sid that singing did not make it rain? __mom__

5. What came down after Sid was done singing? __rain__

6. Who sings with her mom? __Jan__

Sentences: The fox had a bone.
The ram had a cone.

V V V V V V V V V V V V

W W W W W W W W W W W

X X X X X X X X X X X X

Side 2   Spelling: seal, sail, bait, beat

Worksheet

110 Test **11** Name _____

See Teacher's Guide for test remedies.

1. __road__   2. __bait__
3. __seal__   4. __tail__

The mom turtle began to make the batter. She said, "We mix sweet butter into the batter."
But she had bitter butter. And bitter butter won't make a sweet cake.

e   or   ch   ol

1. drink	1. <u>visit</u>ed	1. only
2. <u>ch</u>omp	2. <u>some</u>body	2. biting
3. sh<u>or</u>t	3. <u>be</u>came	3. r<u>e</u>ally
4. t<u>ur</u>n	4. <u>think</u>ing	4. brother

Worksheet

☐ In a while, the sky became dark. The little turtle said, "I think it will start to rain. We need to go home."

☐ But the big turtle said, "No. I will stay here. The sun will come back."
☐ The sun did not come back. Rain came down.

☐ The big turtle said, "I had a sun bath. Now I will have a rain bath. Ho ho."

fold first

fold

Child's choice **110**

Red

☐ Two brown turtles lived in the weeds near a pond.
☐ One day the turtles were sitting on some rocks. The big turtle said, "I really like this sun."

Take Home

60

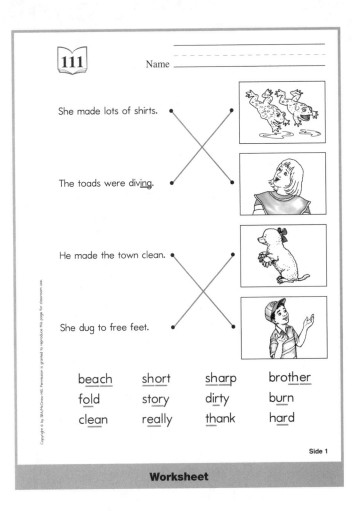

Name _____

She made lots of shirts.

The toads were di<u>ving</u>.

He made the town clean.

She dug to free feet.

beach	short	sharp	brother
fold	story	dirty	burn
clean	really	thank	hard

(underlined: be<u>a</u>ch, <u>sh</u>ort, <u>sh</u>arp, bro<u>th</u>er, fold, story, dirty, burn, clean, <u>really</u>, <u>th</u>ank, <u>h</u>ard)

Side 1

Worksheet

1. On a winter day, her mom showed her how to make **turtles**.
   • cars   • turtles   • soap

2. Did Jan make that same thing over and over? **yes**

3. Her mom said, " **I can't see the rug** ".
   • I can't see the rocks   • I can't see the rug   • I can't see

4. Jan said that she will take the turtles to **the beach**.
   • the farm   • the store   • the beach

5. Who will play with the turtles? **kids**
   • seals   • kids   • goats

6. What did Jan make next? **shirts**
   • shirts   • boats   • bikes

z z z z z z z z z z z z

y y y y y y y y y y y y y

Side 2

Sentences: The fox had a cake.
The ram had a rake.

Spelling: beat, loan, tail, toad

Worksheet

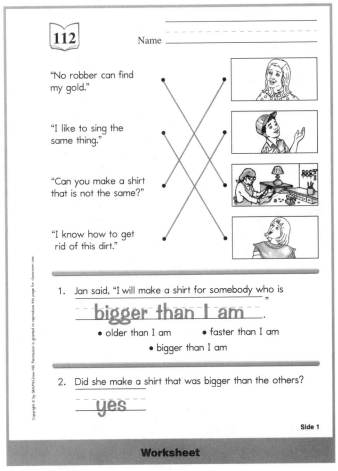

Name _____

"No robber can find my gold."

"I like to sing the same thing."

"Can you make a shirt that is not the same?"

"I know how to get rid of this dirt."

1. Jan said, "I will make a shirt for somebody who is **bigger than I am** ."
   • older than I am   • faster than I am
   • bigger than I am

2. Did she make a shirt that was bigger than the others? **yes**

Side 1

Worksheet

3. Did the bigger shirt have dots on it? **yes**

4. Did that shirt fit somebody? **no**

5. Who said, "That shirt is so big that six moms can fit in it"? **Jan's mom**
   • Bob   • Jan's mom   • Jan

6. What is that shirt on now? **a car**
   • a cow   • a cat   • a car

| reach | mother | sharp | cheap |
| trainer | short | shirt | march |

(underlined: rea<u>ch</u>, mo<u>th</u>er, <u>sh</u>arp, <u>ch</u>eap, trainer, <u>sh</u>ort, <u>sh</u>irt, mar<u>ch</u>)

z z z z z z z z z z z z

s s s s s s s s s s s s s

Side 2

Sentences: The fish is under a boat.
The bird is under a coat.

Spelling: bait, bat, got, goat

Worksheet

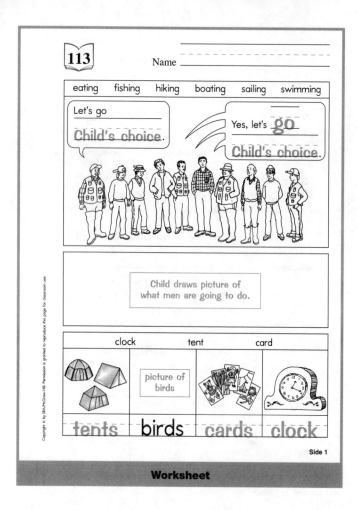

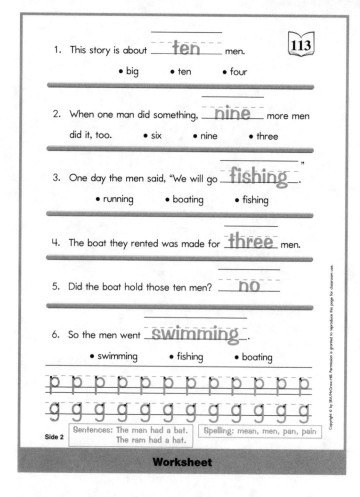

113

1. This story is about _____ten_____ men.
   • big   • ten   • four

2. When one man did something, _____nine_____ more men did it, too.   • six   • nine   • three

3. One day the men said, "We will go _____fishing_____."
   • running   • boating   • fishing

4. The boat they rented was made for _____three_____ men.

5. Did the boat hold those ten men? _____no_____

6. So the men went _____swimming_____.
   • swimming   • fishing   • boating

p p p p p p p p p p p p

g g g g g g g g g g g g

Side 2 | Sentences: The man had a bat. The ram had a hat. | Spelling: mean, men, pan, pain

Worksheet

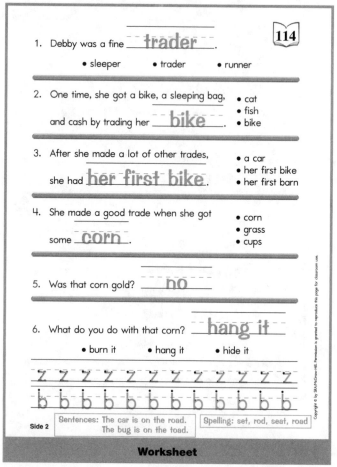

114

1. Debby was a fine _____trader_____.
   • sleeper   • trader   • runner

2. One time, she got a bike, a sleeping bag, and cash by trading her _____bike_____.
   • cat   • fish   • bike

3. After she made a lot of other trades, she had _____her first bike_____.
   • a car   • her first bike   • her first barn

4. She made a good trade when she got some _____corn_____.
   • corn   • grass   • cups

5. Was that corn gold? _____no_____

6. What do you do with that corn? _____hang it_____
   • burn it   • hang it   • hide it

z z z z z z z z z z z z

b b b b b b b b b b b b

Side 2 | Sentences: The car is on the road. The bug is on the toad. | Spelling: set, rod, seat, road

Worksheet

62

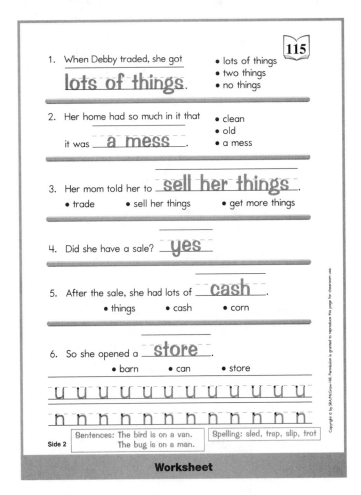

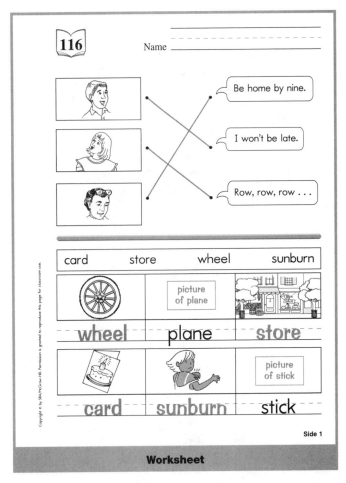

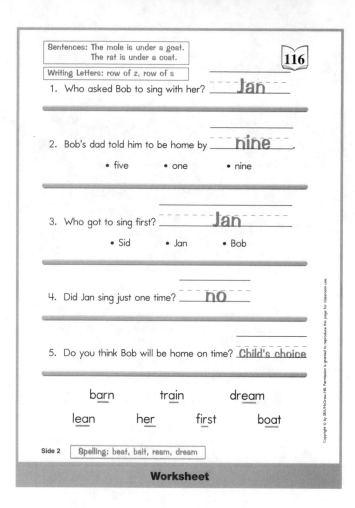

116

Sentences: The mole is under a goat.
The rat is under a coat.

Writing Letters: row of z, row of s

1. Who asked Bob to sing with her? _____Jan_____

2. Bob's dad told him to be home by _____nine_____.
   • five   • one   • nine

3. Who got to sing first? _____Jan_____
   • Sid   • Jan   • Bob

4. Did Jan sing just one time? _____no_____

5. Do you think Bob will be home on time? _Child's choice_

b<u>ar</u>n   tr<u>ai</u>n   dr<u>ea</u>m
l<u>ea</u>n   h<u>er</u>   f<u>ir</u>st   b<u>oa</u>t

Side 2   Spelling: beat, bait, ream, dream

Worksheet

117   Name _____

late   on   not   home   time   nine   by

I hope I am
_____
(Child's choice)

sky	shirt	hat	king

king	sky	picture of cup
king	**sky**	**cup**

shirt	picture of bug	hat
shirt	**bug**	**hat**

Side 1

Worksheet

117

Sentences: The ant is in a cake.
The goat is in a lake.

Letters: s, z, b, d

1. Who got to sing first? _____Jan_____
   • Jan's mom   • Jan   • Bob

2. Who told Jan that Bob needs a turn?
   _____Jan's mom_____
   • Jan's mom   • Bob's dad   • Bob

3. Who was singing, "You are my sunshine"?
   _____Bob_____
   • Jan's mom   • Jan   • Bob

4. Did Bob sing just one time or lots of times?
   _____lots of times_____

5. Did Bob get home on time? _____no_____

6. When will Bob sing with Jan next?
   _____not for a while_____
   • now   • not for a while   • in a while

l<u>oa</u>d   <u>o</u>ver   <u>ea</u>t   pl<u>ay</u>ing
aw<u>ay</u>   start   ch<u>o</u>p   butter

Side 2   Spelling: seal, sail, main, mean

Worksheet

118   Name _____

bitter   fox   tub   better

This butter is
_____better_____.

fox   **tub** (butter)

trail   five   robber   baby   winter

picture of ring	robber	five
ring	**robber**	**five**

winter	baby	trail
winter	**baby**	**trail**

Side 1

Worksheet

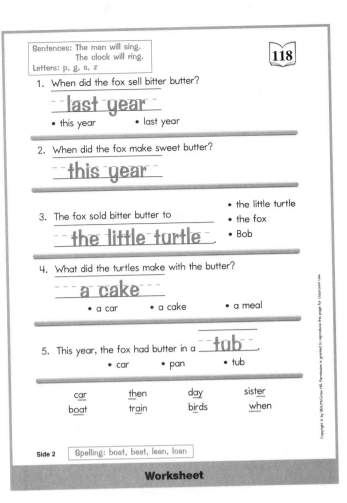

Sentences: The man will sing.
The clock will ring.
Letters: p, g, s, z

1. When did the fox sell bitter butter?

__last year__
• this year   • last year

2. When did the fox make sweet butter?

__this year__

3. The fox sold bitter butter to
__the little turtle__ .
• the little turtle
• the fox
• Bob

4. What did the turtles make with the butter?
__a cake__
• a car   • a cake   • a meal

5. This year, the fox had butter in a __tub__ .
• car   • pan   • tub

car   then   day   sister
boat   train   birds   when

Side 2 | Spelling: boat, beat, lean, loan

Worksheet

Name _____

rat   sweet   fox   bitter   butter

It's __sweet__ .   It's too __bitter__ .

Sweet, sweet
__butter__   __fox__   __rat__

boat   swim   run   eat

__run__   __boat__   __swim__   __eat__

Side 1

Worksheet

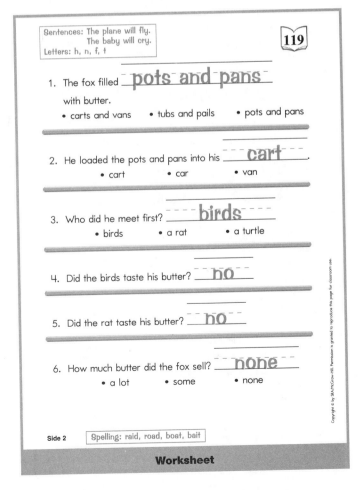

Sentences: The plane will fly.
The baby will cry.
Letters: h, n, f, t

1. The fox filled __pots and pans__
with butter.
• carts and vans   • tubs and pails   • pots and pans

2. He loaded the pots and pans into his __cart__ .
• cart   • car   • van

3. Who did he meet first? __birds__
• birds   • a rat   • a turtle

4. Did the birds taste his butter? __no__

5. Did the rat taste his butter? __no__

6. How much butter did the fox sell? __none__
• a lot   • some   • none

Side 2 | Spelling: raid, road, boat, bait

Worksheet

Name _____

fine   bitter   cake   barn

This __cake__
is __fine__ (yellow).

Yellow

farm   pants   storm   fishing

picture of bed

__pants__   __bed__   __storm__

picture of bag

__fishing__   __farm__   __bag__

Side 1

Worksheet

65

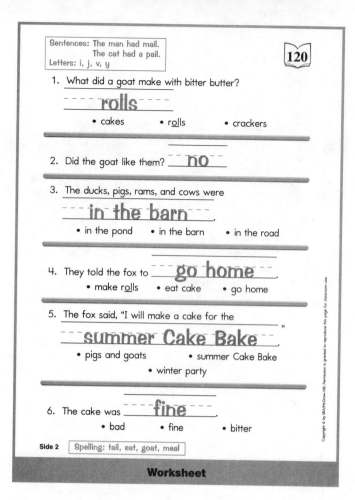

Sentences: The man had mail.
The cat had a pail.
Letters: i, j, v, y

1. What did a goat make with bitter butter?

   rolls
   • cakes   • r_oll_s   • crackers

2. Did the goat like them? **no**

3. The ducks, pigs, rams, and cows were

   in the barn .
   • in the pond   • in the barn   • in the road

4. They told the fox to **go home** .
   • make r_oll_s   • eat cake   • go home

5. The fox said, "I will make a cake for the

   summer Cake Bake ."
   • pigs and goats   • summer Cake Bake
               • winter party

6. The cake was **fine** .
   • bad   • fine   • bitter

Side 2   Spelling: tail, eat, goat, meal

Worksheet

Name _____

picture of fox
with a bone
and ram with
a cone

The fox had a bone.
The ram had a cone.

Take Home

Name _____

dress	fox	cake	cart	hat	wig

wig   **cake**   **dress**

fox   **cart**   **hat**

A cow ate grass. •

A turtle dove into a pond. •

A duck sat on a cow. •

Side 1

Worksheet

Sentences: She had a ring.
He had a rock.
Letters: r, w, o, a

1. What did the fox have on?

   a hat, a dress, and a wig
   • a hat, a dress, and a wig   • a hat, a shirt, and a skirt
         • a wig, a coat, and a tail

2. **20** cakes were in the summer Cake Bake.
   • 50   • 10   • 20

3. Which cake did the cake tasters like best?

   a yellow cake
   • a brown cake   • a yellow cake   • a red cake

4. Who baked that cake? **(the) fox**

5. Will the fox sell lots of sweet butter now? **yes**

6. Now the birds, pigs, rats, cows, and turtles think the

   butter is **fine** .
   • bad   • fine   • bitter

Side 2   Spelling: pal, pail, bat, bait

Worksheet

Name _____

| had | go | flying | sing | am |

I <u>am</u> <u>flying</u> .

Go, Tom, <u>go</u>

| wing | dream | tub | cow |

picture of dress

something colored yellow

<u>tub</u>   <u>dress</u>   <u>yellow</u>

<u>cow</u>   <u>dream</u>   <u>wing</u>

Side 1

Worksheet

Sentences: She will run.
He will swim.
Letters: k, x, v, g

1. Who had a fear of flying? __<u>Tom</u>__

2. Did Tom's brothers and sisters have a fear of flying?
<u>no</u>

3. When did his mother tell Tom it was time for him to fly?
<u>just before summer</u>
- just before winter   • just before spring
- just before summer

4. She told him to jump on her back and <u>hang on</u>
- sleep   • hang on   • sit

5. Did Tom fly? <u>yes</u>

6. Tom's brothers and sisters went flying and had
<u>fun</u>
- fun   • fear   • feet

Side 2   Spelling: men, red, mean, read

Worksheet

Name _____

| birds | summer | ride |

It feels like <u>summer</u>

I am going to see the <u>birds</u> .

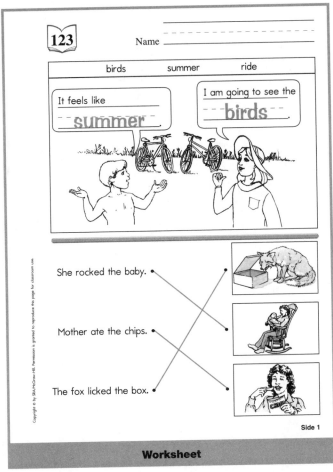

She rocked the baby.

Mother ate the chips.

The fox licked the box.

Side 1

Worksheet

Sentences: The pig had a stick.
The cat had a cup.

1. What was the winter like?
<u>hard and cold</u>
- hard and hot   • hard and cold   • hotter and hotter

2. Irma said, "We have only seen <u>a dark sky</u>"
- a dark sky   • a dark sun   • hills

3. Who said, "I will ride my bike to the lake"? <u>Irma</u>
- Bob   • Irma   • Vern

4. What did Irma plan to see? <u>birds</u>
- birds   • a hill of mud   • goats

5. Who wore a big hat? <u>Irma</u>

6. What was the only thing Vern wore?
<u>short pants</u>
- black pants
- a big hat
- short pants

q q q q q q q q q q q q q

p p p p p p p p p p p p p

Side 2   Spelling: boat, bait, rain, train

Worksheet

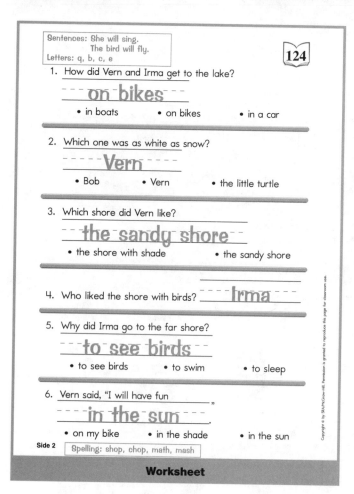

124   Name _____

beach   sun   Vern   lake

sun

lake   Vern   beach

Side 1

Worksheet

Sentences: She will sing.
The bird will fly.
Letters: q, b, c, e

124

1. How did Vern and Irma get to the lake?
   __on bikes__
   • in boats   • on bikes   • in a car

2. Which one was as white as snow?
   __Vern__
   • Bob   • Vern   • the little turtle

3. Which shore did Vern like?
   __the sandy shore__
   • the shore with shade   • the sandy shore

4. Who liked the shore with birds? __Irma__

5. Why did Irma go to the far shore?
   __to see birds__
   • to see birds   • to swim   • to sleep

6. Vern said, "I will have fun
   __in the sun__ "
   • on my bike   • in the shade   • in the sun

Side 2   Spelling: shop, chop, math, mash

Worksheet

125

Dear Mom,
Thank you for
the (new, white)
shirt (with
flowers on it).
Love,
(Child's name)

Lined Paper

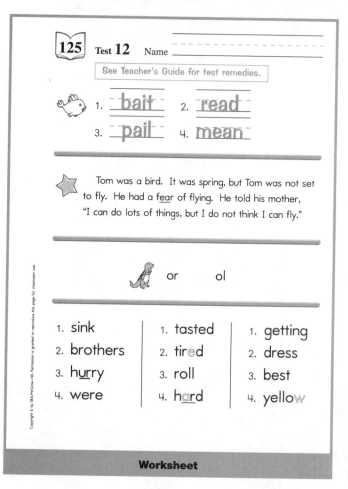

125   **Test 12**   Name _____

See Teacher's Guide for test remedies.

1. bait   2. read
3. pail   4. mean

Tom was a bird. It was spring, but Tom was not set to fly. He had a fear of flying. He told his mother, "I can do lots of things, but I do not think I can fly."

or   ol

1. sink	1. tasted	1. getting
2. brothers	2. tired	2. dress
3. hurry	3. roll	3. best
4. were	4. hard	4. yellow

Worksheet

Take Home — 125

Child folds and takes home.

Each day, Tom's brothers and sisters went flying, but Tom stayed at home.
Each day, the others came home and told what they had. Tom did not have fun.

Then just before summer started, Tom's mom told him, "It's time for you to fly. Jump up on my back and hang on."
He did that. And his mom sailed into the sky.

Then Tom's mother said, "It is more fun if you hold your wings up."
After he did that, was he still on his mom's back? No. He was not on his mom's back. He was flying. And it was fun.
The end.

It was spring. The other birds were set to fly, but Tom was not set to fly.
Tom had a fear of flying. He told his mom, "I can run, and I can read. I can sit, and I can sing. But I do not think I can fly."

126

Name _____

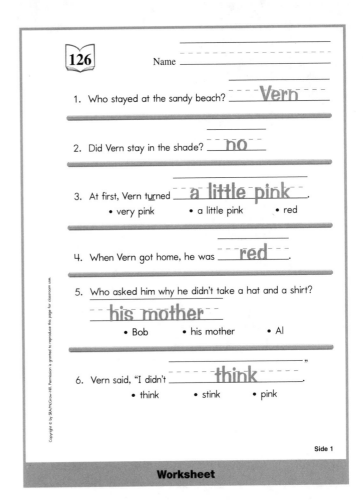

1. Who stayed at the sandy beach? _**Vern**_

2. Did Vern stay in the shade? _**no**_

3. At first, Vern turned _**a little pink**_.
   • very pink   • a little pink   • red

4. When Vern got home, he was _**red**_.

5. Who asked him why he didn't take a hat and a shirt?
   **his mother**
   • Bob   • his mother   • Al

6. Vern said, "I didn't _**think**_."
   • think   • stink   • pink

Worksheet — Side 1

Sentences: The mole will dig.
The fox will sit.
Letters: q, g, n, v

126

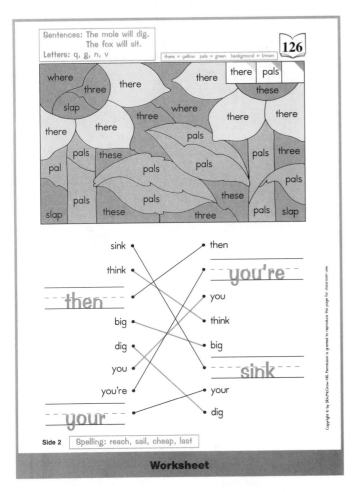

there = yellow   pals = green   background = brown

sink —— then
think —— you're
          you
big —— think
dig —— big
you —— sink
you're —— your
your —— dig

then / you're / sink / your

Side 2   Spelling: reach, sail, cheap, last

Worksheet

127

Name _____

pail   goat   fox   toad   pig

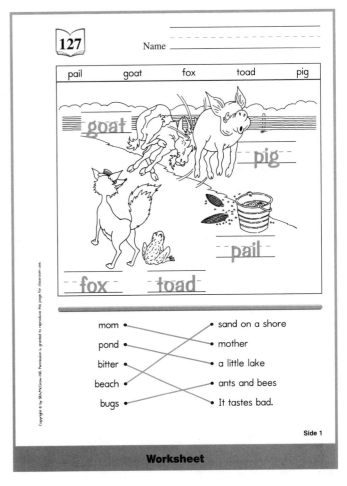

goat   pig   pail   fox   toad

mom • — • sand on a shore
pond • — • mother
bitter • — • a little lake
beach • — • ants and bees
bugs • — • It tastes bad.

Worksheet — Side 1

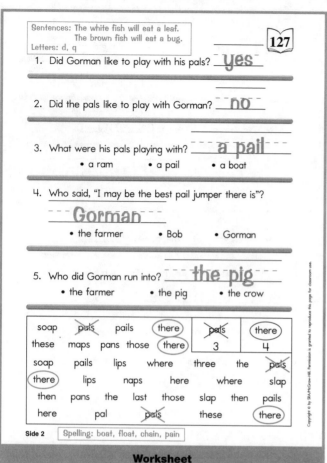

Worksheet 127

Sentences: The white fish will eat a leaf.
The brown fish will eat a bug.
Letters: d, q

1. Did Gorman like to play with his pals? __yes__

2. Did the pals like to play with Gorman? __no__

3. What were his pals playing with? __a pail__
   • a ram   • a pail   • a boat

4. Who said, "I may be the best pail jumper there is"?
   __Gorman__
   • the farmer   • Bob   • Gorman

5. Who did Gorman run into? __the pig__
   • the farmer   • the pig   • the crow

soap	~~pals~~	pails	(there)		~~pals~~	(there)
these	maps	pans	those	(there)	3	~~4~~
soap	pails	lips	where	three	the	~~pals~~
(there)	lips	naps	here	where	slap	
then	pans	the	last	those	slap	then	pails
here	pal	~~pals~~		these		(there)

Side 2   Spelling: boat, float, chain, pain

Worksheet

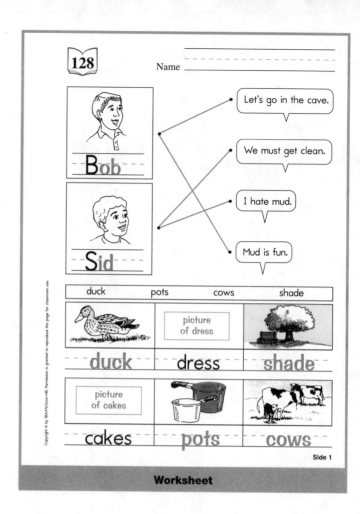

128

Name _____

Bob
Sid

Let's go in the cave.
We must get clean.
I hate mud.
Mud is fun.

| duck | pots | cows | shade |

__duck__   __dress__   __shade__

__cakes__   __pots__   __cows__

Side 1

Worksheet

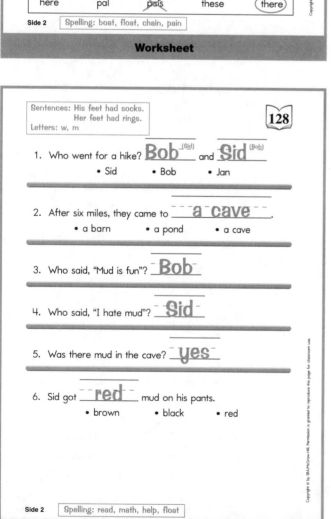

128

Sentences: His feet had socks.
Her feet had rings.
Letters: w, m

1. Who went for a hike? __Bob__ (Sid) and __Sid__ (Bob)
   • Sid   • Bob   • Jan

2. After six miles, they came to __a cave__
   • a barn   • a pond   • a cave

3. Who said, "Mud is fun"? __Bob__

4. Who said, "I hate mud"? __Sid__

5. Was there mud in the cave? __yes__

6. Sid got __red__ mud on his pants.
   • brown   • black   • red

Side 2   Spelling: read, math, help, float

Worksheet

129

Name _____

| not | seal | swimming | got | go | hard |

This mud is __not__ __hard__.

Let's __go__ __swimming__

happy •   • many miles away
plane •   • not sad
trees •   • You can fly in it.
far •   • They have leaves.

Side 1

Worksheet

70

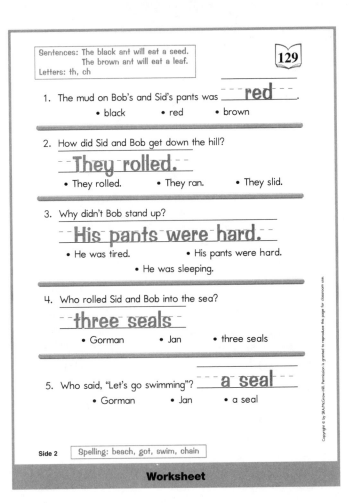

Sentences: The black ant will eat a seed.
The brown ant will eat a leaf.
Letters: th, ch

129

1. The mud on Bob's and Sid's pants was ___red___.
   - black • red • brown

2. How did Sid and Bob get down the hill?
   ___They rolled.___
   - They rolled. • They ran. • They slid.

3. Why didn't Bob stand up?
   ___His pants were hard.___
   - He was tired. • His pants were hard.
   - He was sleeping.

4. Who rolled Sid and Bob into the sea?
   ___three seals___
   - Gorman • Jan • three seals

5. Who said, "Let's go swimming"? ___a seal___
   - Gorman • Jan • a seal

Side 2 | Spelling: beach, got, swim, chain |

Worksheet

130   Name _____

| clam | fun | hang | otter | on |

Hang on .

Fun , fun .

clam

otter

hug • — • not hard
easy • — • to hold with your arms
liked • — • not clean
dirty • — • not hated

Side 1

Worksheet

Sentences: The bird was on a rope.
The bug was on a rug.
Letters: wh, sh

130

1. Ann was a ___clam___.
   - shark • clam • fish

2. Ann said, "Why can't I swim with ___otters___"?
   - sharks • fish • otters

3. Otters like to eat ___clams___.
   - sharks • goats • clams

4. Ann told an otter to hide from ___a shark___.
   - a clam • Bob • a shark

5. Who takes Ann swimming? ___an otter___
   - her mom • an otter • a shark

| shell | summer | saw |
| shell | saw | summer | fish |

picture of
a fish or
someone fishing

Side 2 | Spelling: pink, train, trap, end |

Worksheet

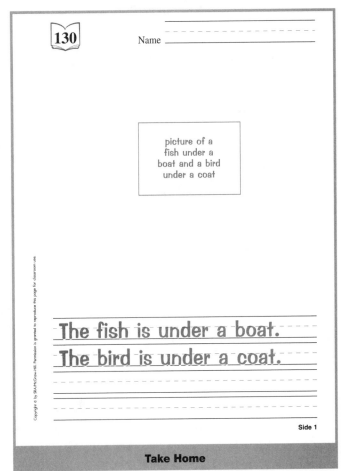

130   Name _____

picture of a
fish under a
boat and a bird
under a coat

The fish is under a boat.
The bird is under a coat.

Side 1

Take Home

131

Name _____

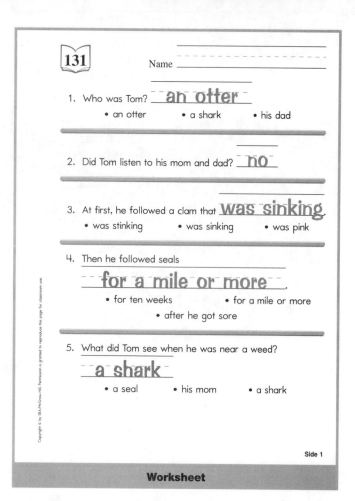

1. Who was Tom? __an otter__
   • an otter   • a shark   • his dad

2. Did Tom listen to his mom and dad? __no__

3. At first, he followed a clam that __was sinking__
   • was stinking   • was sinking   • was pink

4. Then he followed seals
   __for a mile or more__.
   • for ten weeks   • for a mile or more
           • after he got sore

5. What did Tom see when he was near a weed?
   __a shark__
        • a seal   • his mom   • a shark

Side 1

Worksheet

131

Sentences: The box was in a lake.
The kite was in the sky.
Letters: ar, ol

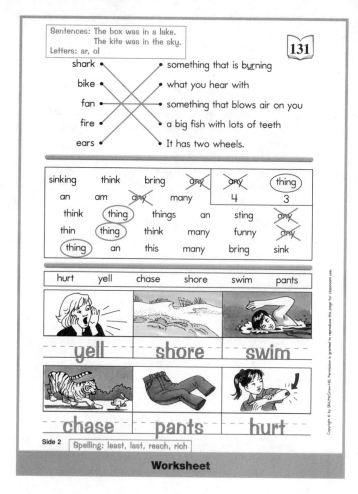

shark • — • something that is burning
bike • — • what you hear with
fan • — • something that blows air on you
fire • — • a big fish with lots of teeth
ears • — • It has two wheels.

sinking	think	bring	~~any~~		~~any~~	(thing)
an	am	~~any~~	many		4	3
think	(thing)	things	an		sting	~~any~~
thin	(thing)	think	many		funny	~~any~~
(thing)	an	this	many		bring	sink

| hurt | yell | chase | shore | swim | pants |

__yell__   __shore__   __swim__

__chase__   __pants__   __hurt__

Side 2   Spelling: least, last, reach, rich

Worksheet

132

Name _____

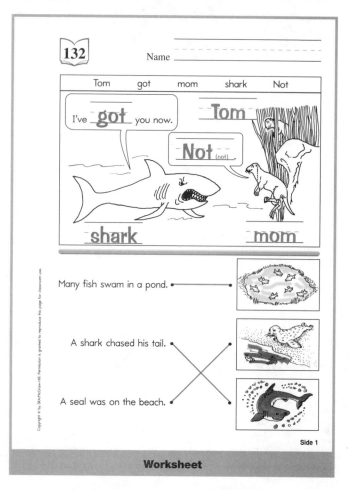

| Tom | got | mom | shark | Not |

I've __got__ you now.   __Tom__

__Not__ (not)

__shark__   __mom__

Many fish swam in a pond. •
A shark chased his tail. •
A seal was on the beach. •

Side 1

Worksheet

132

Sentences: The fish was in a lake.
The bug was on a snake.
Letters: or, ea

1. Which otter yelled from beneath?
   __Tom's mom__
   • Tom   • Tom's mom   • Tom's dad

2. Who bit the shark's tail? __Tom's mom__

3. Which otter did the shark chase? __Tom's mom__

4. Tom's mom stopped __in front of a rock__.
   • in a cave   • in front of a rock   • to eat

5. Was Tom shocked? __yes__

farm • — • jump
hive • — • not slow
easy • — • a home for cows, sheep, and goats
leap • — • a home for bees
fast • — • not hard

Side 2   Spelling: lean, blast, cheat, heat

Worksheet

72

Name _____

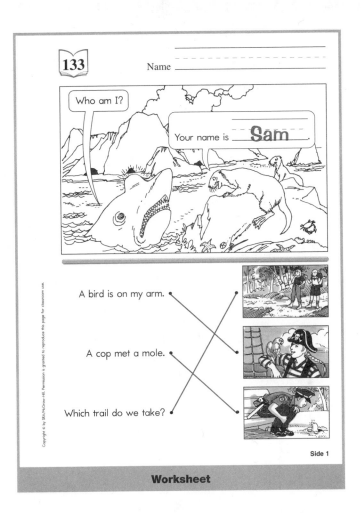

Who am I?

Your name is **Sam** .

A bird is on my arm.

A cop met a mole.

Which trail do we take?

Side 1

Worksheet

Sentences: She had a brown hat.
He had a brown cat.
Letters: oa, ch

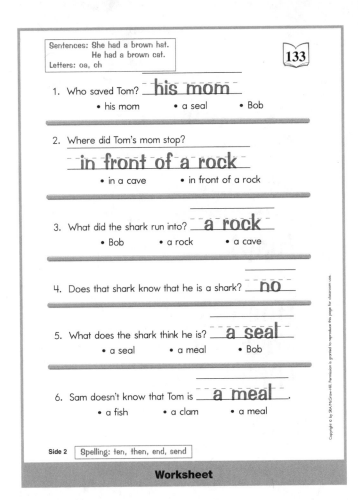

1. Who saved Tom? **his mom**
   • his mom   • a seal   • Bob

2. Where did Tom's mom stop?
   in front of a rock
   • in a cave   • in front of a rock

3. What did the shark run into? **a rock**
   • Bob   • a rock   • a cave

4. Does that shark know that he is a shark? **no**

5. What does the shark think he is? **a seal**
   • a seal   • a meal   • Bob

6. Sam doesn't know that Tom is **a meal** .
   • a fish   • a clam   • a meal

Side 2 | Spelling: ten, then, end, send |

Worksheet

Name _____

| soak | you | help | save |

We'll **save** **you** .

Help , {help} **help**

| tractor | shell | swimming | street |

street   **tractor**   **smile**

picture of a smile or someone smiling

shell   **men**   **swimming**

picture of men

Side 1

Worksheet

Sentences: The rat was on a barn.
The duck was on a rug.
Letters: ea, wh

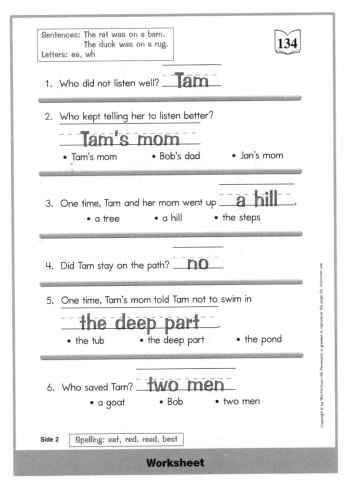

1. Who did not listen well? **Tam**

2. Who kept telling her to listen better?
   Tam's mom
   • Tam's mom   • Bob's dad   • Jan's mom

3. One time, Tam and her mom went up **a hill**
   • a tree   • a hill   • the steps

4. Did Tam stay on the path? **no**

5. One time, Tam's mom told Tam not to swim in
   the deep part
   • the tub   • the deep part   • the pond

6. Who saved Tam? **two men**
   • a goat   • Bob   • two men

Side 2 | Spelling: eat, red, read, best |

Worksheet

135

Dear (name),
Can you come
see a play in
our classroom?
(day)
(time)
(theme)
Your pal,
(Child's name)

Lined Paper

---

135 Test 13 Name _____

1. **end** 2. **red**
3. **beach** 4. **cheat**

Bob and Sid went inside a cave. Sid said, "I feel my feet sinking in mud. Let's go." In a little while, they came from the cave. "We must get clean before that mud gets hard."

1. shark	1. very	1. saw
2. snail	2. shell	2. doesn't
3. street	3. chased	3. many
4. swam	4. himself	4. because

Worksheet

"Shark, shark. Hide, hide."

A little otter was swimming near the clams, too. The little otter did not see the shark. As the otter came close to Ann, she opened her shell and yelled,

One day, a shark was swimming near the clams.

Ann said, "Why can't I swim with clams." Others eat clams. They don't swim with clams."

Her mom said, "That's silly. Why can't I swim with the otters?"

A little otter was swimming near the clams,

The little otter hid in the weeds, and the shark went away. The next day, the otter came back. She said to the cl... saving me... in return?...

You kn... said, and... they did.

So if y... otter swi... on its tail... who they are.

The end.

Child completes and takes home.

fold first

fold

135

(Child's choice)

Clams seem to have a big smile, but some clams are not happy. One sad clam was named Ann. Why was she sad? She did not like to stay in the sand with the other clams.

Take Home

---

136 Name _____

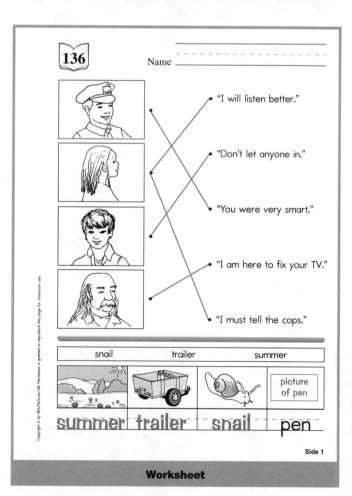

"I will listen better."

"Don't let anyone in."

"You were very smart."

"I am here to fix your TV."

"I must tell the cops."

| snail | trailer | summer |

summer **trailer** **snail** **pen**

picture of pen

Side 1

Worksheet

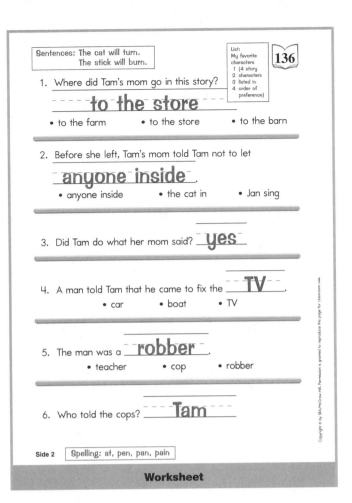

136

Sentences: The cat will turn.
The stick will burn.

List: My favorite characters
1 (4 story characters
2 characters
3 listed in
4 order of preference)

1. Where did Tam's mom go in this story?
___to the store___
• to the farm   • to the store   • to the barn

2. Before she left, Tam's mom told Tam not to let
___anyone inside___.
• anyone inside   • the cat in   • Jan sing

3. Did Tam do what her mom said? ___yes___

4. A man told Tam that he came to fix the ___TV___.
• car   • boat   • TV

5. The man was a ___robber___.
• teacher   • cop   • robber

6. Who told the cops? ___Tam___

Side 2   Spelling: at, pen, pan, pain

Worksheet

137   Name ___

trailer   home   tractor   this   Bob

We are on the way ___home___
I can run faster than ___this___.
___tractor___
___trailer___

☑ 1. Make a T over the tree.
☑ 2. Make an O under the tree.
☑ 3. Make a T on the fish.

T
O

Side 1

Worksheet

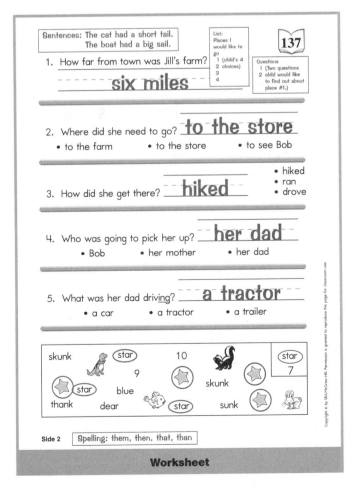

137

Sentences: The cat had a short tail.
The boat had a big sail.

List: Places I would like to go
1 (child's 4
2 choices)
3
4

Questions
1 (Two questions
2 child would like
to find out about
place #1.)

1. How far from town was Jill's farm?
___six miles___

2. Where did she need to go? ___to the store___
• to the farm   • to the store   • to see Bob

3. How did she get there? ___hiked___
• hiked
• ran
• drove

4. Who was going to pick her up? ___her dad___
• Bob   • her mother   • her dad

5. What was her dad driving? ___a tractor___
• a car   • a tractor   • a trailer

skunk   star   10
9   star
star   skunk
thank   blue   sunk   star
dear   7

Side 2   Spelling: them, then, that, than

Worksheet

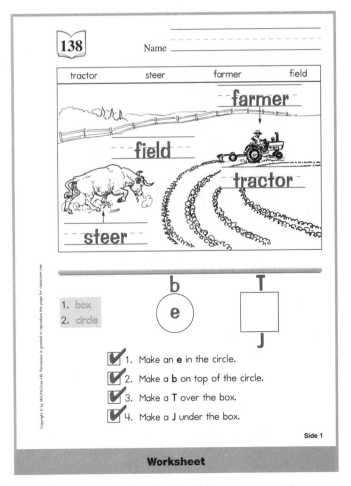

138   Name ___

tractor   steer   farmer   field

___farmer___
___field___
___tractor___
___steer___

1. box
2. circle

b
e
T
J

☑ 1. Make an e in the circle.
☑ 2. Make a b on top of the circle.
☑ 3. Make a T over the box.
☑ 4. Make a J under the box.

Side 1

Worksheet

75

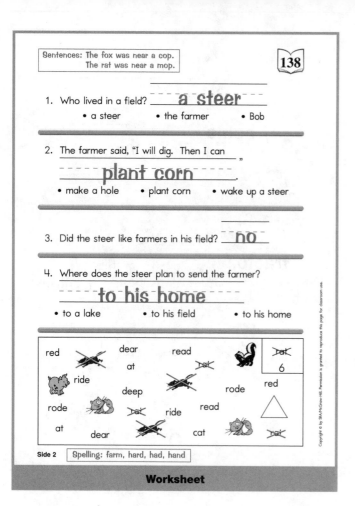

Sentences: The fox was near a cop.
The rat was near a mop.

138

1. Who lived in a field? __a steer__
   • a steer   • the farmer   • Bob

2. The farmer said, "I will dig. Then I can __plant corn__."
   • make a hole   • plant corn   • wake up a steer

3. Did the steer like farmers in his field? __no__

4. Where does the steer plan to send the farmer?
   __to his home__
   • to a lake   • to his field   • to his home

red   dear   read
       at
ride   deep   rode   red
rode   ride   read
at   dear   cat   6

Side 2   Spelling: farm, hard, had, hand

Worksheet

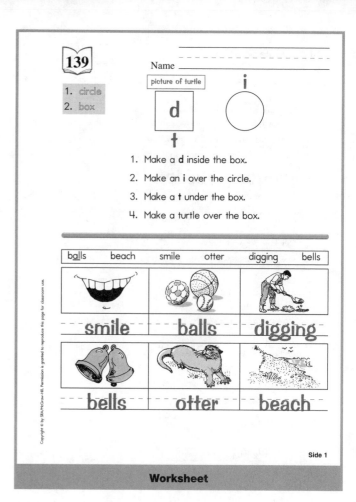

139

Name _____

1. circle
2. box

picture of turtle   i

d
t

1. Make a **d** inside the box.
2. Make an **i** over the circle.
3. Make a **t** under the box.
4. Make a turtle over the box.

| balls | beach | smile | otter | digging | bells |

smile   balls   digging

bells   otter   beach

Side 1

Worksheet

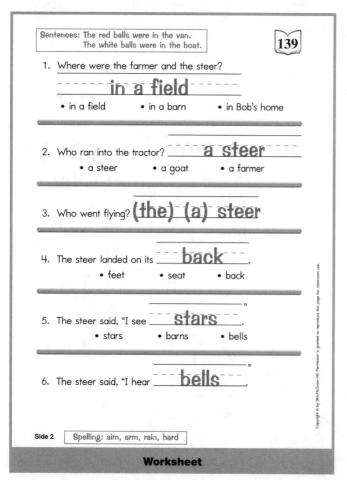

Sentences: The red balls were in the van.
The white balls were in the boat.

139

1. Where were the farmer and the steer?
   __in a field__
   • in a field   • in a barn   • in Bob's home

2. Who ran into the tractor? __a steer__
   • a steer   • a goat   • a farmer

3. Who went flying? __(the) (a) steer__

4. The steer landed on its __back__.
   • feet   • seat   • back

5. The steer said, "I see __stars__."
   • stars   • barns   • bells

6. The steer said, "I hear __bells__."

Side 2   Spelling: aim, arm, rain, hard

Worksheet

140

Name _____

| dad | stones | Sandy | throw |

I don't like to __throw__ __stones__.

dad   Sandy

little ———— what you hear with
grab ———— take
snow ———— small
ears ———— It's cold and white.
stones ———— small rocks

Side 1

Worksheet

76

Worksheet 140 (Side 2)

Sentences: She spoke to a black bird.
He spoke to a red bird.

140

List:
a Anna
b Bill
c Carl
d Donna

1. Sandy did not know how to **throw** .
   • roll   • swim   • throw

2. Did she try to throw balls and stones? **no**

3. Who asked her to throw stones in the lake?
   her dad
   • her mom   • her dad   • her brother

4. Who asked her to throw snow balls?
   her brother

5. Sandy and her brother were in the **front yard** .
   • back yard   • street   • front yard

6. What hit her in the back? **a snow ball**
   • a hand   • a snow ball   • a snow man

Side 2   Spelling: tail, tar, part, paint

Worksheet

Lesson 140 Take Home — Page 1

140

Tom and the Shark

There once was an otter, and his name was Tom.
But Tom didn't listen to his dad or mom.

One day his mom told him, "Don't swim near the caves.
Because there's a shark who hunts in those waves."

But Tom started playing, and he wasn't really thinking.
He first chased a clam that seemed to be sinking.

Then he followed two seals that were close to the shore.
He followed those seals for a mile or more.

At last he stopped to see where he was.
He said, "I saw something swimming the way a shark doe

"Oh, oh," he said, as he hid near a weed.
"I hope this is not where sharks like to feed."

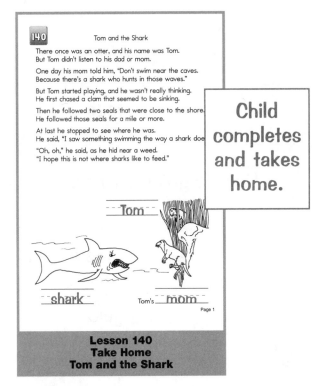

Tom a

shark   Tom's **mom**

Page 1

> Child completes and takes home.

Lesson 140
Take Home
Tom and the Shark

Lesson 140 Take Home — Page 2

140

But the shark came closer and showed many teeth.
And just at that moment, someone yelled from beneath.

"For a bigger meal, you can come after me."
The otter who spoke was Tom's mom, you see.

She swam and she dove and bit the shark's tail.
She told that shark, "You're as slow as a snail."

The shark chased Tom's mom as fast as a shot.
And said, "I've got you now." But Tom's mom said, "Not."

Just then Tom got a very bad shock.
His mom just stopped, in front of a rock.

As the shark came closer, did she stay where she was?
No, she darted to one side, the way an otter does.

The shark hit the rock with such a hard blow,
That he said to himself, "Who am I? I don't know."

Then he asked Tom's mom, "Can you tell me who I am?"
She said, "You're a very big seal, and your name is Sam."

So Tom has a pal who thinks he's a seal.
And Sam doesn't know that Tom is a meal.

The end.

Page 2

Lesson 140
Take Home
Tom and the Shark

Worksheet 141 (Side 1)

141   Name

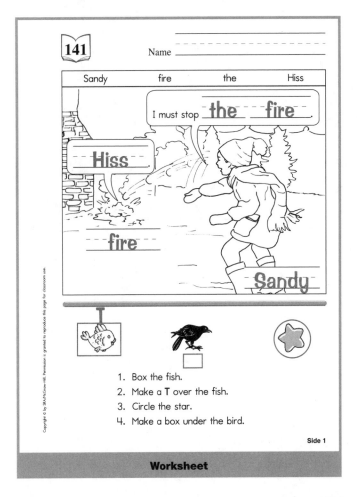

Sandy   fire   the   Hiss

I must stop **the** **fire** .

Hiss .

fire

Sandy

1. Box the fish.
2. Make a **T** over the fish.
3. Circle the star.
4. Make a box under the bird.

Side 1

Worksheet

Worksheet 141 — Side 2

Sentences: The cat licked a hand.
The cow licked an ear.

List:
Things I like to eat
1 (Child's
2 4
3 choices
4 here)

141

1. What did Sandy see in the back yard? **a fire**
   • a skunk   • a fire   • a tree

2. What made the fire start? **a spark**
   • a spark   • the sun   • a storm

3. What was burning at first? **rags**
   • leaves   • sticks   • rags

4. Why didn't Sandy's brother help her stop the fire?
   He was going for help.
   • He didn't see her.   • He didn't hear her.
   • He was going for help.

5. What did Sandy throw at the fire? **snow balls**
   • baseballs   • snow flakes   • snow balls

6. Can Sandy throw things now? **yes**

Side 2   Spelling: art, eat, aim, team

Worksheet

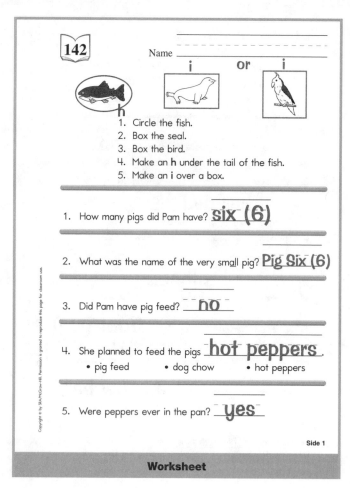

142

Name _____

i   or   i

h

1. Circle the fish.
2. Box the seal.
3. Box the bird.
4. Make an **h** under the tail of the fish.
5. Make an **i** over a box.

1. How many pigs did Pam have? **six (6)**

2. What was the name of the very small pig? **Pig Six (6)**

3. Did Pam have pig feed? **no**

4. She planned to feed the pigs **hot peppers**.
   • pig feed   • dog chow   • hot peppers

5. Were peppers ever in the pan? **yes**

Side 1

Worksheet

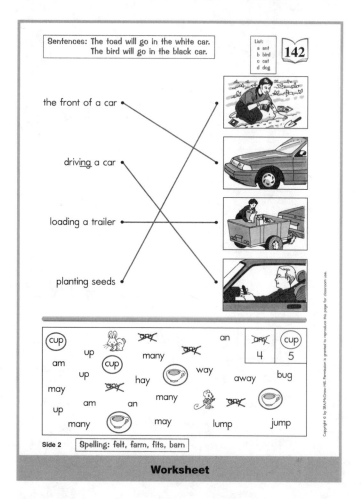

Sentences: The toad will go in the white car.
The bird will go in the black car.

List:
a ant
b bird
c cat
d dog

142

the front of a car •

driving a car •

loading a trailer •

planting seeds •

cup   up   many   an   cup   4   5
am   up   cup   way
may   am   an   away   bug
up   many   many   lump   jump
many   may

Side 2   Spelling: felt, farm, fits, barn

Worksheet

143

Name _____

Color little pig pink, others red.

Pig
Pam
Six
Burp

Burp

Pig Six   **Pam**

5   u

1. Make a **U** in front of the bird.
2. Make a **5** in back of the car.
3. Circle the barn.
4. Box the bird.

Side 1

Worksheet

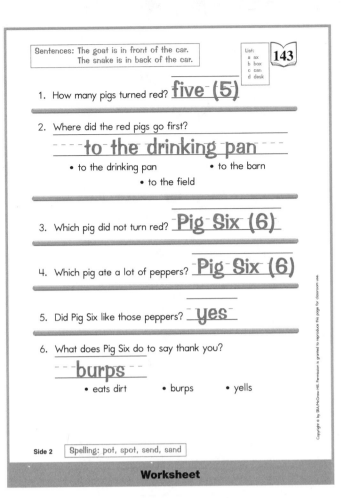

Sentences: The goat is in front of the car.
The snake is in back of the car.

List:
a ax
b box
c can
d desk

143

1. How many pigs turned red? **five (5)**

2. Where did the red pigs go first?
   to the drinking pan
   • to the drinking pan   • to the barn
   • to the field

3. Which pig did not turn red? **Pig Six (6)**

4. Which pig ate a lot of peppers? **Pig Six (6)**

5. Did Pig Six like those peppers? **yes**

6. What does Pig Six do to say thank you?
   burps
   • eats dirt   • burps   • yells

Side 2 | Spelling: pot, spot, send, sand

Worksheet

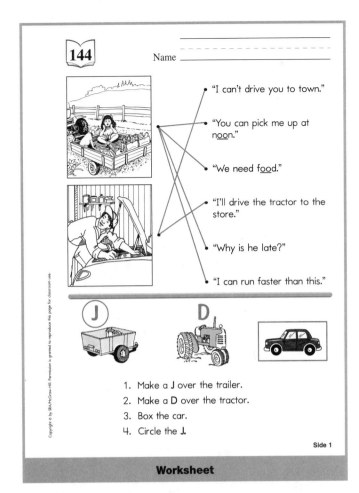

144   Name _____

"I can't drive you to town."

"You can pick me up at noon."

"We need food."

"I'll drive the tractor to the store."

"Why is he late?"

"I can run faster than this."

J   D

1. Make a **J** over the trailer.
2. Make a **D** over the tractor.
3. Box the car.
4. Circle the **J**.

Side 1

Worksheet

Sentences: The fish is in front of the boat.
The seal is in front of a goat.

List:
c cat
d dog
e eagle
f fox

144

1. Jill lived **six (6)** miles from town.

2. What was her dad fixing? **a car**
   • a trailer   • a car   • a tractor

3. How did Jill get to the store? **She hiked.**
   • She ran.   • She swam.   • She hiked.

4. Did she have to wait for her dad? **yes**

5. What was he driving? **a tractor**
   • a cart   • a truck   • a tractor

pool	drink	steer

drink | **ball** | **steer** | **pool**

Side 2 | Spelling: men, man, top, stop

Worksheet

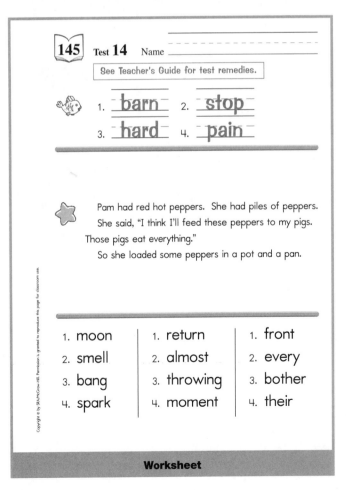

145   Test **14**   Name _____

See Teacher's Guide for test remedies.

1. **barn**   2. **stop**
3. **hard**   4. **pain**

Pam had red hot peppers. She had piles of peppers.
She said, "I think I'll feed these peppers to my pigs.
Those pigs eat everything."
So she loaded some peppers in a pot and a pan.

1. moon	1. return	1. front
2. smell	2. almost	2. every
3. bang	3. throwing	3. bother
4. spark	4. moment	4. their

Worksheet

Food for Three

Jill lived on a farm that
was six miles from town.

Page 1

**Lesson 145
Take Home
Food for Three**

Soon she saw him.
Was he driving the car?
No. He was driving a
tractor with a trailer.
Jill loaded her bags into
the trailer, and her dad
drove them home.

The end.

Page 4

**Lesson 145
Take Home
Food for Three**

Child completes and takes home.

Jill told her dad, "It is time
to go to the store for food."
"Well," her dad said, "I
need to fix the car. So I
can't drive you there now."
Jill said, "I have a plan. I
can hike to the store. You
can pick me up at noon."

Page 2

So Jill hiked to the store.
When she got there, she got
a cart and filled it with food.
She waited for her dad in
front of the store. He didn't
show up. She began to
think of things that may
have made her dad late.

Page 3

**Lesson 145
Take Home
Food for Three**